FRENCH
VERBS MADE EASY
WORKBOOK

*Learn French Verbs and
Conjugations The Easy Way*

Lingo Mastery

ISBN: 978-1-951949-72-3

Copyright © 2023 by Lingo Mastery

CONTENTS

CONTENTS

PREFACE: ABOUT THE LANGUAGE
PRÉFACE: À PROPOS DE LA LANGUE FRANÇAISE

A foreign language is an essential communication tool for the modern era. Nowadays, French is the seventh-most widely spoken language globally, with 267 million people speaking it to varying degrees. Studies indicate that French is one of the most used languages on social networks, with 3.3 billion users.

French, a Romance language, is widely regarded as among the most beautiful languages in the world. Today, many people think that French is no longer useful, that the language is less and less spoken. Well, this is totally false! Although it is true that the French language no longer holds the same place in the world now compared to the 19th century, it still plays a significant role and is the second most learned language in the world after English.

French is also among the top languages in countries where it holds an official status. Alongside English, it is also the only language taught in every country in the world, and it is the only language (besides English) that's spoken in every continent (much of West Africa is French-speaking, Canada in North America, French Guiana in South America, Vanuatu in Oceania).

WHY LEARN FRENCH?
POURQUOI APPRENDRE LE FRANÇAIS ?

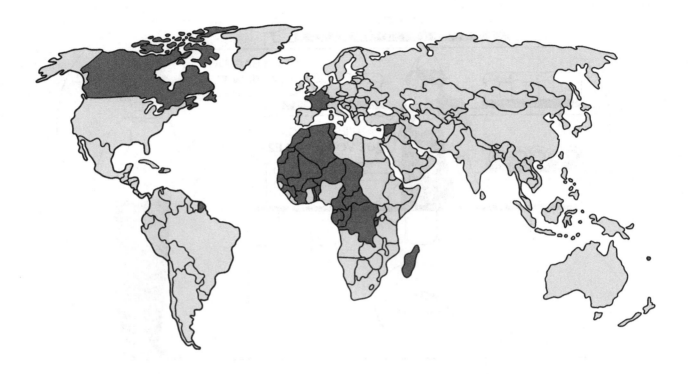

a) For work

Of course, nowadays, English is the primary language used around the world in a work environment! However, since almost everyone speaks English, it's no longer considered a "plus", but the minimum required. On the other hand, knowing how to speak French is an undeniable "plus" for your CV! It will set you apart from other candidates.

b) To live and travel to France and other French-speaking countries

France is the most visited country in the world! Canada is also an amazing country to explore. Even as a tourist, knowing how to speak the language is always better! Besides, the French speak very few foreign languages... So, if you want to live in France or a French-speaking country, there is no arguing: you will have to learn the language.

c) For your personal enrichment

Learning a language means getting to know another culture, getting to know other people and what better way to broaden your horizons! Especially if you speak a language like French! French and France are all about culture, knowledge, ideas, history, curiosity, enlightenment...

d) You will be able to speak with many more people around the world

Indeed, French is still spoken in many countries and by many people worldwide: France, Canada, Belgium, Switzerland, Maghreb countries, etc. Moreover, their number is increasing every day.

e) You will meet interesting and cultured people!

French is the language of culture. If you speak French, you will be able to access information from and about interesting people, for example, on the Internet. You will also be able to communicate in everyday life with people who often have different, creative ideas.

To learn a language, it is crucial to have good educational resources, and books are one of the best materials—they are essential tools to achieve our goals. Therefore, finding the right resource is important, and you need the one that best suits your needs and goals. Apart from the content, the book should also be attractive and have a clear design.

This is what we are offering you with the French Verbs Made Easy Workbook.

STRUCTURE
STRUCTURE

There are efficient methods that will allow you to learn French in a self-taught and independent manner. These methods include complete support materials designed to approach every aspect of the French language: written and oral comprehension and written and oral expression. A suitable method allows you to progress in French while having fun. The method will, ideally, simulate real-life situations. If you want to learn to communicate quickly in French, this is the book for you!

This book will introduce you to the French conjugation in a solid and effective manner, giving you the linguistic, cultural, and strategic tools to communicate and to continue moving forward. This self-study tool will focus on the formal aspects of the language only as they relate to how the language is used. You will learn key concepts for the use of verbs in French. This book is based on scientific research, which has shown that the most effective way to remember verbs and their conjugation is by stimulation and not by learning whole tables of verbs by heart. In most grammar books, you will find gigantic black and white tables to learn by heart. You will **not** find those here. This method aims to stimulate and entertain you while you learn.

This book will cover all aspects of French conjugation to cater to your specific needs in your learning journey. It is designed for learners at a beginner to intermediate proficiency level.

The activities have been selected to enhance communicative, linguistic, thematic, and learning domains. They include texts, cultural and linguistic information to strengthen your knowledge of the language.

If you want to move to the next level in conversation, reading, and writing while developing your grammar and conjugation skills, this book is designed for you!

Of course, while "French Verbs Made Easy" can be used for self-study, it can also be used as a supplement as part of a teacher-led course.

Once you are confident with the content of this book, congratulate yourself because you will have acquired solid foundations for the rest of your learning journey. Mastering the fundamentals of French conjugation is something that can take years. It is a challenge with which even native speakers can struggle their entire life.

Finally, for best results, we also advise studying the French Made Easy Level 1 and the French Picture Dictionary books by Lingo Mastery.

INTRODUCTION

INTRODUCTION

The pedagogical approach adopted in the book is centered on a vision of language as a place of interaction, as a mediating dimension of the relationships established between subjects and different cultural worlds. Language does not just mean a form or system, but a set of possibilities for interaction and experience that includes not only formal structures and their rules, but also all the social, cultural, historical, and political meanings that constitute it.

Learning French means living cultural and linguistic experiences in a new language, thinking in this new language and the student's own mother tongue. It also means considering the student as an active subject.

This first level has for objective the development of communication and interaction skills at the initial level, in the production and reception of oral and written genres of low and medium complexity. It prepares the student to interact in French in everyday situations in different contexts.

Among the reasons to study and learn French is the possibility of communicating with French speakers in your community, making your travel experiences more rewarding and exciting, enhancing your jobs prospects, improving and understanding your own language better, enjoying French music, literature, films, and theater in their original form.

RECOMMENDATIONS
RECOMMANDATIONS

The book is best for learners with an A1+/A2 level in the Common European Framework of Reference for Languages (CEFR), corresponding to a beginner-basic level. It is a tool for anyone motivated to learn French. After finishing this book, you will master French conjugation at an A2+ level and will understand what you need to focus on in the next levels. Let us give you some interesting recommendations and tips:

Imposter syndrome is real when learning a foreign language, especially when learning about French conjugation. Mistakes happen: We all make mistakes, especially when learning a new language, but that should not discourage us; on the contrary, it should encourage us to learn from our mistakes.

It sometimes seems difficult to remember words when learning a language, but it does not mean that you have completely forgotten them; they are still somewhere in your mind. Practice will allow you to reduce the time you need to remember words. This book will help you in this process by practicing as much as possible.

You do not need to rush, as everyone works at their own pace. Take your time; you will learn everything. And please, do not feel frustrated or disappointed if some concepts or units take more time than others.

Last but not least, practice makes perfect!

PRONUNCIATION GUIDE
GUIDE DE PRONONCIATION

This section is a reminder of what you should already know at an A1 – A2 level.

However, in case you are not familiar with French pronunciation or need to review some concepts, we advise reviewing the alphabet and pronunciation section of the French Made Easy Level 1 by Lingo Mastery.

ALPHABET
L'ALPHABET

UPPER-CASE	LOWER-CASE	PRONUNCIATION	IPA
A	a	*Ah*	*[a]*
B	b	*Bay*	*[b]*
C	c	*Say*	*[se]*
D	d	*Day*	*[de]*
E	e	*Eh*	*[ə]*
F	f	*Ef*	*[ɛf]*
G	g	*Jay*	*[ʒe]*
H	h	*Ash*	*[aʃ]*
I	i	*Ee*	*[i]*
J	j	*Jee*	*[ʒi]*
K	k	*Kah*	*[ka]*
L	l	*El*	*[ɛl]*
M	m	*Em*	*[ɛm]*

N	n	En	[ɛn]
O	o	Oh	[o]
P	p	Pay	[pe]
Q	q	Queue	[ky]
R	r	Air	[ɛʁ]
S	s	Es	[ɛs]
T	t	Tay	[te]
U	u	Uh	[y]
V	v	Vay	[ve]
W	w	Doobleh-vay	[dublave]
X	x	Eeks	[iks]
Y	y	Ee-grec	[i gʁɛk]
Z	z	Zed	[zɛd]

VOWELS

LES VOYELLES

A → sounds like *ah* → as in *cat, patate*

E/EU → sounds like *euh* → as in *fur, pleuvoir*

É → sounds like *hey* → as in *café*

È/Ê → sounds like *hay* → as in *pair, air*

I/Y → sounds like *ee* → as in *pit, difficile*

O/AU/EAU → sounds like *oh* → as in *paw, gâteau*

OI → sounds like *wah* → as in *swan, poire*

U → sounds like *u* → as in *tutu, uber*

OU → sounds like *oo* → as in *fool, poule*

CONSONANTS

LES CONSONNES

C + E/I/Ç → sounds like *ss* → as in *center, ici, ça va?*

C + other letters → sounds like *kah* → as in *catastrophe, combien*

CH → sounds like *sh* → as in *shell, marche*

G + E/I → sounds like *je* → as in *giraffe, gîte*

G + other letters → sounds like *geh* → as in *grass, grammaire*

GN → sounds like *nyeh* → as in *champagne, campagne*

H → is *silent!* → as in *heir, hôtel*

QU → sounds like *keh* → as in *key, quiche*

LL → sounds like *elle* → as in *belle, ville* → sounds like *yeh* → as in *fille, je travaille*

A FEW MORE RULES

In French, you pronounce **j, b, d, p, t** more softly than in English, while the letter **r** is rolled a lot more.

Usually, in French, the last consonant of a word is not sounded (chat = *cha*, chaud = *cho*).

When a word ends in an s and is followed by a vowel, you should link both sounds together. This is called a *liaison* :

Les enfants ont mangé des bonbons = Les**z**enfants ont mangé des bonbons.

INTRODUCTION TO FRENCH CONJUGATION
INTRODUCTION À LA CONJUGAISON FRANÇAISE

A language can be considered a form of art, providing tools and concepts for expressing meaning, intention, emotions, and many other things.

It encompasses various aspects, including:

    a) the **sounds of human speech** (phonetics),

    b) the **use of speech** (phonology),

    c) the **internal structures of words** (morphology),

    d) the **study of words** and their relationships (lexicology),

    e) **spelling** (orthographic linguistics),

    f) the **rules for constructing sentences** (syntax),

g) the **study of meaning** in a language (semantics),

h) the **study of language from the users' viewpoint,** how words are used in context, how their meanings differ based on who is speaking, etc. (pragmatics).

Now, you may be wondering, what does this all have to do with conjugation? In order to understand what conjugation is and what verbs are, this small overview is necessary. Verbs are closely connected to how words change their forms, which we call morphology.

In simpler terms, when we conjugate a verb, we modify its form to express different grammatical aspects, such as tense, person, or mood. For example, in English:

Present tense:

a) *I do* vs. *I did:* we modify the verb to express a different tense.

b) *I go* vs. *He goes:* we modify the verb to express a different person.

Conjugation in itself can almost be considered an art. Indeed, conjugating verbs properly requires you to choose the correct form of the verb. This is achieved by also choosing the correct person and the correct tense. When you finish this book, you will have built upon solid foundations and will be ready to safely continue your journey onto the B1+/B2 levels, or intermediate levels.

Before reading this book, you may have attempted to read rather complex French content with a dictionary by your side, but even then, you were not able to find the meanings of some verbs because you did not understand what they were, their form, or their tense. At the end of this book, no matter what verb you stumble upon, you shall be able to find it in the dictionary as well as its meaning.

French conjugation has a bad reputation. Verbs have **96 forms**. Verbs can have even more forms in other languages, though. Besides, most of those forms can be deduced relatively straightforwardly in French. For example, for most compound forms, one only needs to know the past participle of the verb, which auxiliary verb comes with it, and how to conjugate the auxiliary verb. If you do not understand what an auxiliary verb and a past participle mean, do not worry, we have you covered. You will understand all those concepts after studying this book.

WHAT ARE VERBS?
QUE SONT LES VERBES ?

This seems like a funny question, right? But the truth is we use verbs every day, yet most of us do not even know how to define a verb. In linguistics, a verb can be defined as a word that adds the notion of tense to its own meaning. The present time and verbs are intrinsically connected. The present time thus constitutes the speaker's reference system when using verbs. Verbs allow us to depict time (tense) and express duration (aspect).

FORM
FORME

The form is what enables us to distinguish verbs from nouns in French. Verbs are the only words that can be conjugated. In this context, conjugation can be defined as all the forms a verb can have.

MEANING
SIGNIFICATION

Verbs express states, actions, and changes of state, which all depend on the subject:

a) The car enters the tunnel. (Action)

b) The driver is really tired. (State)

c) The house is burning. (Change of state)

SYNTAX
SYNTAXE

From a syntactic perspective, the verb plays one of the most important roles in speech. A language without verbs would be quite limited.

LOGIC
LOGIQUE

Verbs allow us to add logical information to our sentences. For example:

a) "The car" means nothing concrete. "The car broke" does. The verb "to break" adds the missing information to the sentence.

b) "The bird" means nothing concrete in itself either, but "The bird sings" does.

HOW TO GET THE AUDIO FILES

Some of the exercises throughout this book come with accompanying audio files. You can download these audio files if you head over to
www.lingomastery.com/french-vme-audio

This headphone symbol behind the heading of a text, dialogue or exercise indicates that audio content is available for the corresponding section.

This headphone with a pencil next to an exercise means that you will need to refer to the corresponding audio content to complete the exercise.

THE BASICS
LES BASES

In this section, we will cover some of the most fundamental aspects of French grammar and conjugation. At an A1 – A2 level, it is expected that students already know those fundamentals, as they are the foundations of the language. The goal is to have a clear idea and structure of those fundamentals so that you can build on them after that.

TO BE / TO HAVE

ÊTRE / AVOIR

CONJUGATION OF THE VERB "ÊTRE" (TO BE)
IN THE PRESENT TENSE OF THE INDICATIVE MOOD
CONJUGAISON DU VERBE ÊTRE AU PRÉSENT DE L'INDICATIF

To be,
or not
to be.

REMINDER

"On" in French means **one** as, for example: **one** does not speak in class. "On" in French is also the informal "we", although it is conjugated like "il" and "elle". The word **it** is expressed differently, for example: **c'**est bien/**it** is good. While we try to avoid using endless lists and tables, there are some cases where it is absolutely necessary for you to learn them by heart. You should know the following table by heart, or at least know how to recognize them.

ÊTRE	TO BE
je suis	I am
tu es	you are
il / elle / on est	he / she / it is
nous sommes	we are
vous êtes	you are
ils / elles sont	they are

CONJUGATION OF THE VERB "AVOIR" (TO HAVE) IN THE PRESENT TENSE OF THE INDICATIVE MOOD
CONJUGAISON DU VERBE AVOIR AU PRÉSENT DE L'INDICATIF

The same goes as for the verb "to have", you should also know the following table very well or at least know how to recognize the different forms.

AVOIR	TO HAVE
j'ai	I have
tu as	you have
il / elle / on a	he / she / it has
nous avons	we have
vous avez	you have
ils / elles ont	they have

USAGE
USAGE

Être (to be) is generally used to express a state (e.g., to be sad), behavior (e.g., to be selfish) or action (e.g., to be late), for example:

a) Je suis malade aujourd'hui.
I am sick today.

b) Tu es content d'avoir eu ton permis de conduire.
You are happy that you passed your driver's license.

c) Elle est au volant de sa voiture de course.
She is behind the wheel of her racing car.

d) Nous sommes en retard à cause des embouteillages.
We are late because of traffic jams.

e) Vous êtes sages en amphithéâtre à l'université, c'est bien.
You behave well in the lecture hall at university, that is good.

f) Les enfants sont agités aujourd'hui.
The children are restless today.

Avoir (to have) is generally used to express possession (e.g., I have a dog), for example:

a) J'ai une nouvelle voiture grâce à mon travail.
I have a new car thanks to my work.

b) Tu as un bel ordinateur.
You have a beautiful computer.

c) On n'a pas très faim pour le moment.
We are not very hungry at the moment.

d) Vous avez une grande famille.
You (pl.) have a big family.

e) Nous avons des amis formidables.
We have fantastic friends.

f) Elles ont des livres sur l'art et la science.
They (fem.) have books about art and science.

Expressing Age:

a) Quel âge as-tu ?
How old are you?

b) J'ai vingt ans.
I am twenty years old.

Expressing Hunger:

a) J'ai faim.
I am hungry.

b) Il a toujours faim !
He is always hungry!

EXERCISES
EXERCICES

1) Conjugate the verb être correctly.

Conjuguez le verbe être correctement.

a) Je _____ épuisé aujourd'hui avec le travail. / *I am exhausted because of work today.*

b) Tu _____ bien silencieux aujourd'hui. / *You are rather quiet today.*

c) On _____ arrivé en avance à la gare ce matin. / *We arrived early at the train station this morning.*

d) Nous _____ plutôt contents des résultats de notre entreprise. / *We are quite happy with the results of our company.*

e) Vous _____ très doués à ce jeu, bravo! / *You are very talented at this game, well done!*

f) Elles _____ très rapides en course à pied. / *They (fem. pl.) are very fast runners.*

2) Conjugate the verb avoir correctly.

Conjuguez le verbe avoir correctement.

a) J' _____ un chien. / *I have a dog.*

b) Tu _____ de belles lunettes de soleil. / *You have beautiful sunglasses.*

c) Elle _____ des amis sympathiques. / *She has nice friends.*

d) Nous _____ un ordinateur que nous pouvons te prêter. / *We have a computer that we can lend you.*

e) Vous _____ une très belle maison et de belles fleurs. / *You (pl.) have a beautiful house and beautiful flowers.*

f) Ils _____ acheté une baguette, du fromage et un peu de vin rouge. / *They (masc. pl.) bought a baguette, some cheese and a little bit of red wine.*

3) Underline the correct form of the verb
Soulignez la forme du verbe qui correspond

a) **J'ai / Je suis** heureuse. / *I am happy (fem. sing.).*

b) Nous **avons / sommes** du fromage pour le déjeuner. / *We have some cheese for lunch.*

c) Apparemment, ces écoliers **n'ont / ne sont** pas école aujourd'hui. / *Apparently, these pupils do not have class today.*

d) Vous **avez / êtes** du lait. / *You have milk.*

e) Mon collègue de travail **a / est** les yeux verts. / *My work colleague (masc.) has green eyes.*

f) Tu **es / as** un nouveau livre. / *You have a new book.*

g) Elles **sont / ont** une jolie bougie. / *They (fem. pl.) have a beautiful candle.*

h) Parfois, **j'ai / je suis** trop fatigué pour travailler. / *Sometimes, I am too tired to work.*

i) On **a / est** malade depuis hier. / *We have been sick since yesterday.*

j) Mon professeur **est / a** un doctorat en chimie. / *My professor has a PhD in chemistry.*

k) Ton ordinateur **est / a** bleu et rose. / *Your computer is blue and pink.*

l) Sa maison **est / a** très grande. / *His/Her house is very big.*

m) Les nuages **ont / sont** des formes bizarres. / *Clouds have strange shapes.*

n) Mars **a / est** des montagnes très hautes. / *Mars has very high mountains.*

o) Ils **ont / sont** dans la même classe. / *They are in the same class.*

p) Ma sœur **a / est** quarante-trois (43) ans. / *My sister is forty-three (43) years old.*

q) **Avoir / Être** ou ne pas **avoir / être**, telle est la question. / *To be or not to be, that is the question.*

r) Un ami **a / est** une personne amicale. / *A friend is a friendly person.*

s) Louis **a / est** un roi de l'histoire de France. / *Louis is a king in French history.*

t) Mes chats **sont / ont** toujours faim. / *My cats are always hungry.*

INFINITIVE

INFINITIF

The infinitive form of a verb is when the verb is in its **unconjugated form**, for example: **aller, dormir, manger, boire, appeler**, etc. The infinitive form is a different and special form for verbs. One can recognize infinitive verbs because they end in "**er**", "**ir**", "**oir**" or "**re**". Its form never changes, neither with time nor with subjects. Every verb has only one infinitive.

NOTE
When you look up a verb in the dictionary, it will always be in its infinitive form.

The infinitive form is used after the following prepositions: **à**, *de*, *pour*, and *sans*.

For example:

    a) à: Je réussis **à résoudre** ce problème mathématique.
      I manage to solve this math problem.

    b) de: J'ai envie **de manger** des tartines au beurre et à la confiture.
      I want to eat toasted bread with butter and jam.

c) pour: Jean-François n'a pas de voiture **pour aller** en ville.
   Jean-François does not have a car to go into town.

d) sans: Les gens traversent parfois la rue **sans regarder** à gauche et à droite.
   People sometimes cross the road without looking left and right.

Verbs are also used in their infinitive form when they are placed **after a conjugated verb**.

For example:

a) Je veux **boire** du thé à la menthe avec mes biscuits.
   I want to drink some mint tea with my biscuits.

b) J'aime **danser** avec mes amis.
   I like to dance with my friends.

c) Je vais **marcher** dans la forêt presque tous les jours au printemps.
   I go and have a walk in the forest almost every day in spring.

GENERAL RULE
When a verb follows another verb, then it is used in its infinitive form.

The infinitive form of a verb can also be used at the **beginning of a sentence**. It then acts as the subject of the sentence.

For example:

a) Lire est une de mes passions principales dans la vie.
   Reading is one of my main passions in life.

b) Regarder la télévision ne m'intéresse absolument pas.
   I am not interested in watching television whatsoever.

c) Écouter les oiseaux chanter me rend tellement heureux.
   Listening to chirping birds makes me so happy.

d) Cuisiner de bons petits plats est mon activité préférée en hiver.
   Cooking comfort food is my favorite activity in winter.

EXERCISES
EXERCICES

1) Listen and underline the infinitive form of the verb. (Find audio on page 14.)
Écoutez et soulignez le verbe à l'infinitif.

a) mangent, manger, mangez, mangeons *(to eat)*

b) cours, courons, courir, courent *(to run)*

c) avoir, as, ont, avez *(to have)*

d) faire, faites, fais, fassiez *(to do / to make)*

e) comptes, compter, comptez, comptent *(to count)*

f) écoutes, écoutons, écoutez, écouter *(to listen)*

2) Underline the infinitive form of the verb. *Soulignez le verbe à l'infinitif.*

a) Peux-tu m'aidé / m'aider à porter mes bagages ? / *Can you help me carry my luggage?*

b) Marcher / Marché trop lentement m'ennuie. / *Walking too slowly makes me feel bored.*

c) Avant de dormir / dormi, je révise mes cours de français. / *Before going to bed, I revise my French lessons.*

d) Va vu / voir si la tondeuse à gazon est dans le jardin. / *Go and see if the lawnmower is in the garden.*

e) Les scientifiques permettent de découvert / découvrir des choses merveilleuses. / *Thanks to scientists, we discover wonderful things.*

f) Pour soyons / être en forme, nous devons faire de l'exercice régulièrement. / *In order to stay fit, we must exercise regularly.*

g) Je vais cuisiner / cuisiné un délicieux repas pour mes amis ce soir. / *I am going to cook a delicious meal for my friends tonight.*

h) J'aime fait / faire de la peinture le dimanche après-midi. / *I like painting on Sunday afternoons.*

i) Je ne passe jamais une journée d'été sans nager / nagé dans ma piscine. / *I never spend a summer day without swimming in my pool.*

j) Je vais monter / monté un meuble pour ma cousine. / *I am going to assemble a piece of furniture for my cousin (fem.).*

REGULAR / IRREGULAR
RÉGULIER / IRRÉGULIER

This section aims to help you understand that there are regular and irregular verbs in French and how to recognize them.

In French, **regular verbs** are verbs that keep the same stem (also known as the root) for all their conjugated forms.

Irregular verbs are verbs whose stem, or root, or radix, change depending on the mood, tense, or even subject. In later units, you will learn more about the different moods and tenses in French.

Most verbs whose infinitive end with **er** or **ir** are regular verbs in French. However, French is known for its exceptions: some verbs whose infinitive form ends in **er** or **ir** can also be irregular. Besides, all verbs whose infinitive ends with **re** or **oir** are irregular verbs.

Before being able to conjugate a French verb, we need to know whether the verb belongs to the **first, second, or third group**.

  a) The **first group** is made of verbs ending in **er** except for the verb aller (*to go*).

  b) The **second group** is made of verbs ending in **ir** and whose participle end with **issant.**

  c) All other verbs belong to the **third group**, including aller, verbs ending in **ir** but whose participle end with **ant** only, and all verbs ending in **oir** and **re.**

We will come back to the concepts of regular and irregular verbs thoroughly later, especially with more exercises, but for now, you should know that when we talk about regular verbs, we refer to the first two groups, which follow relatively straightforward conjugation rules.

The third group is made of all irregular verbs. The conjugation of those verbs does not follow uniform patterns. There are only about 350 verbs in this category.

FUN FACT

Nowadays, when new verbs are created, they are always regular. Therefore, they always belong to either the first or second group, which means the third group is never updated anymore. We call this concept "**conjugaison morte**" *(dead conjugation)* in French.

PRESENT TENSE CONJUGATION OF REGULAR VERBS
CONJUGAISON DES VERBES RÉGULIERS AU PRÉSENT

In this section, you will learn how to conjugate regular verbs or verbs that belong to the first group in the present tense.

Do not be scared of the tables. They are almost all the same. We also provide you with two examples each time to get used to recognizing the different forms. In the best case, you should learn the endings of the present tense for regular verbs, or of the first group, by heart. Once you know those six endings, you will be able to conjugate most French verbs in the present tense.

In order to conjugate verbs that belong to the first group, you just have to remove the ending, which is **er**, and keep what remains, also known as the **root**. Then, you can add the different endings, which are as follows:

PERSONAL PRONOUNS *PRONOMS PERSONNELS*	ENDINGS *TERMINAISONS*
je *(I)*	**e**
tu *(you, sing.)*	**es**
il/elle/on *(he/she/it)*	**e**
nous *(we)*	**ons**
vous *(you, pl.)*	**ez**
ils/elles *(they)*	**ent**

REMINDER

When a verb starts with a vowel (a, e, i, o, u), the first person is then j' and not je (e.g., **j'oublie** / I forget).

---

1) Conjugation of a verb of the first group without any additional rule or exception

First example:

ACCEPTER	TO ACCEPT
Radical : **accept**	Root: **accept**
j'accept**e**	I accept
tu accept**es**	you accept
il/elle/on accept**e**	he/she/it accepts
nous accept**ons**	we accept
vous accept**ez**	you accept
ils/elles accept**ent**	they accept

Second example:

FERMER	TO CLOSE
Radical : **ferm**	Root: **ferm**
je ferm**e**	I close
tu ferm**es**	you close
il/elle/on ferm**e**	he/she/it closes
nous ferm**ons**	we close
vous ferm**ez**	you close
ils/elles ferm**ent**	they close

2) Verbs ending in "cer"

In the case of verbs ending in **cer**, e.g.,: commencer *(to begin / to start)*, the **c** is replaced by a **ç** in front of the **ons** ending. This may seem complicated, but in order to remember that easily, remember that this rule exists so that the word still has the same sound as in its infinitive form, that is /**s**/ instead of /**k**/, **e.g**.,:

a) The infinitive form of **commencer** is pronounced ko-man-Seh (/komãse/)

b) **Nous commencons** would be pronounced as ko-man-Kon (/komãkɔ̃/).

c) **Nous commençons** is pronounced as ko-man-Son (/komãsɔ̃/) with /s/ like in the infinitive form.

Second example:

PRONONCER	TO PRONOUNCE
Radical : **prononc**	Root: **prononc**
je prononc**e**	I pronounce
tu prononc**es**	you pronounce
il/elle/on prononc**e**	he/she/it pronounces
nous pronon**çons**	we pronounce
vous prononc**ez**	you pronounce
ils/elles prononc**ent**	they pronounce

3) Verbs ending in "ger"

For verbs which end in **ger** like manger (to eat), we add an **e** before **ons** for the first-person plural, e.g.,: nous mang**e**ons. The reason is the same as in the previous part. The objective is to keep the same sound as in the infinitive form, that is /ʒ/ instead of /g/. For example:

   a) The infinitive form of **manger** is pronounced as man-Jeh (/mɑ̃ʒe/)

   b) Nous mangons would be pronounced as man-Gon (/mɑ̃gɔ̃/)

   c) Nous mangeons is pronounced as man-Jon (/mɑ̃ʒɔ̃/)

Example:

JUGER	TO JUDGE
Root : **jug**	Root: **jug**
je jug**e**	I judge
tu jug**es**	you judge
il/elle/on jug**e**	he/she/it judges
nous jug**eons**	we judge
vous jug**ez**	you judge
ils/elles jug**ent**	they judge

4) Verbs ending in "e/é" + consonant + "er"

The second to last **é** or **e** in verbs ending in **é** + consonnant + **er** (e.g., **référer** / to refer) and those ending in **e** + consonnant + **er** (e.g., **acheter** / to buy) change to **è** when the ending is silent, that is before the following endings: **e**, **es**, and **ent**.

First example:

PRÉFÉRER	TO PREFER
Root : **préfér**	Root: **préfér**
je préfèr**e**	I prefer
tu préfèr**es**	you prefer
il/elle/on préfèr**e**	he/she/it prefers
nous préfér**ons**	we prefer
vous préfér**ez**	you prefer
ils/elles préfèr**ent**	they prefer

Second example:

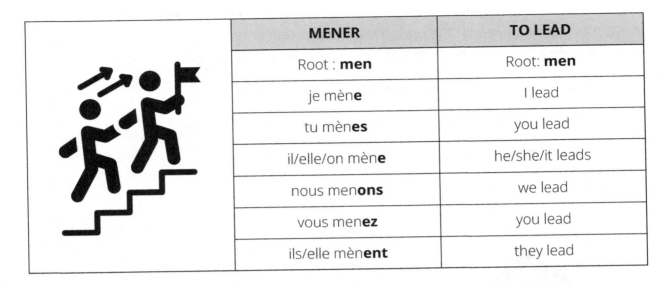

MENER	TO LEAD
Root : **men**	Root: **men**
je mèn**e**	I lead
tu mèn**es**	you lead
il/elle/on mèn**e**	he/she/it leads
nous men**ons**	we lead
vous men**ez**	you lead
ils/elle mèn**ent**	they lead

5) Verbs ending in "eter" or "eler"

The second to last **e** in most verbs, which end with **eter** or **eler** (e.g., **jeter** / *to throw*, or **appeler** / *to call*) does not turn into **è**, like in the previous case. However, the last consonant is doubled if the ending is silent.

Be careful, we saw an exception in the previous case: **acheter**. The verb **modeler** also belongs to the previous category. That is their second to last **e** turns into **è**.

First example:

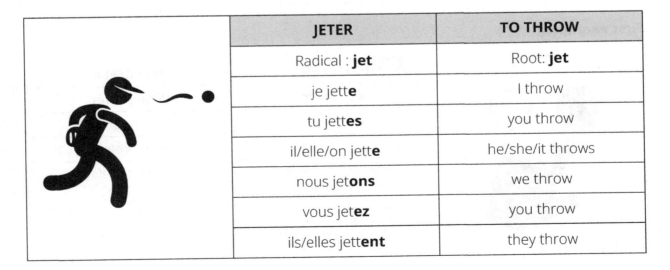

JETER	TO THROW
Radical : **jet**	Root: **jet**
je jett**e**	I throw
tu jett**es**	you throw
il/elle/on jett**e**	he/she/it throws
nous jet**ons**	we throw
vous jet**ez**	you throw
ils/elles jett**ent**	they throw

Second example:

APPELER	TO CALL
Radical : **appel**	Root: **appel**
j'appell**e**	I call
tu appell**es**	you call
il/elle/on appell**e**	he/she/it calls
nous appel**ons**	we call
vous appel**ez**	you call
ils/elles appell**ent**	they call

6) Verbs ending in "oyer" and "uyer"

The y in verbs ending in **oyer** and **uyer** (e.g., **nettoyer** / *to clean*, **ennuyer** / *to annoy, to bother* or *to bore)* turns into an i when the ending is silent.

First example:

NETTOYER	TO CLEAN
Root : **nettoy**	Root: **nettoy**
je nettoi**e**	I clean
tu nettoi**es**	you clean
il/elle/on nettoi**e**	he/she/it cleans
nous nettoy**ons**	we clean
vous nettoy**ez**	you clean
ils/elles nettoi**ent**	they clean

Second example

ENNUYER	TO ANNOY
Radical : **ennuy**	Root: **ennuy**
j'ennui**e**	I annoy
tu ennui**es**	you annoy
il/elle/on ennui**e**	he/she/it annoys
nous ennuy**ons**	we annoy
vous ennuy**ez**	you annoy
ils/elles ennui**ent**	they annoy

Verbs ending in "ayer"

Verbs ending in **ayer** (e.g., **payer** / *to pay*) can be conjugated in two different manners. You can choose the form you like best and use it. You can either choose to turn the **y** into an **i** when the ending is silent, or you can keep the **y**.

First way of conjugating the verb "payer"

	PAYER	TO PAY
	Radical : **pay**	Root: **pay**
	je pai**e**	I pay
	tu pai**es**	you pay
	il/elle/on pai**e**	he/she/it pays
	nous pay**ons**	we pay
	vous pay**ez**	you pay
	ils/elles pai**ent**	they pay

Second way of conjugating the verb "payer"

PAYER	PAY
Radical : **pay**	Root: **pay**
je pay**e**	I pay
tu pay**es**	you pay
il/elle/on pay**e**	he/she/it pays
nous pay**ons**	we pay
vous pay**ez**	you pay
ils/elles pay**ent**	they pay

7) Conjugation of verbs that belong to the second group: general rules

Verbs that belong to the second group follow the same principles. We remove the **ir** ending of the verb to obtain the root (or stem, or radix). Then we add the following endings to conjugate them in the present tense.

je *(I)*	**is**
tu *(you)*	**is**
il/elle/on *(he/she/it)*	**it**
nous *(we)*	**issons**
vous *(you)*	**issez**
ils/elles *(they)*	**issent**

First example:

FINIR	TO FINISH
Radical : **fin**	Root: **fin**
je fin**is**	I finish
tu fin**is**	you finish
il/elle/on fin**it**	he/she/it finishes
nous fin**issons**	we finish
vous fin**issez**	you finish
ils/elles fin**issent**	they finish

Second example:

ROUGIR	TO BLUSH
Radical : **roug**	Root: **roug**
je roug**is**	I blush
tu roug**is**	you blush
il/elle/on roug**it**	he/she/it blushes
nous roug**issons**	we blush
vous roug**issez**	you blush
ils/elles roug**issent**	they blush

Apart from that, verbs belonging to the second group do not have any particularity, which means you can apply this rule to all of them.

PRESENT TENSE CONJUGATION OF IRREGULAR VERBS
CONJUGAISON DES VERBES IRRÉGULIERS AU PRÉSENT

Irregular verbs belong to the last category: **the third group**.

In the previous section of this unit, you learned about regular verbs and how to conjugate them in the present tense. You should know them well as there are almost no exceptions. Now, you are going to learn about irregular verbs.

However, unlike the previous section, the purpose of this one is not to teach you (just yet) how to conjugate them but rather how to recognize them and their conjugation in the present in case you encounter them in sentences.

The root (or stem or radix) is rarely regular. It may even change within a same tense in the third group. If we wanted to divide the verbs of this category further, we could say that the majority of verbs that belong to the third group are more or less irregular but that some verbs are completely irregular.

Amongst verbs we could define as **completely** irregular are the two auxiliary verbs **être** *(to be)* and **avoir** *(to have)*, which you saw previously as well as some verbs like **aller** *(to go)*, **dire** *(to say)*, **faire** *(to do / to make)*, **savoir** *(to know)*, **valoir** *(to be worth)*, and **vouloir** *(to want)*.

That way, when it is your turn to conjugate them yourself in future sections, you will already know many of their forms in the present tense, and you will find the process intuitive and natural.

As you may have just noticed in the verbs we just mentioned, possible endings for the verbs belonging to the third group are **ir**, **ïr**, **oir** and **re**.

Verbs of the third group ending in **ir** or **ïr** do not end with **issons** or **issez** in the first - and second-person plural. Some examples of such verbs are: **acquérir** *(to acquire)*, **bouillir** *(to boil)*, **dormir** *(to sleep)*, **fuir** *(to flee / to escape)*, **mentir** *(to lie)*, **ouïr** *(to listen, formal)*, **ouvrir** *(to open)*, **partir** *(to leave)*, and **venir** *(to come)*.

Verbs which end with **oir** are less numerous than those which end with **ir**. Some common examples are: **asseoir** (also spelled as **assoir**, *to sit*), **avoir** *(to have)*, **devoir** *(must)*, **pleuvoir** *(to rain)*, **pouvoir** *(can / to be able to)*, **recevoir** *(to receive)*, **savoir** *(to know)*, **valoir** *(to be worth)*, **vouloir** *(to want)*, **voir** *(to see)*, etc.

1) Present tense
   Le présent

As we briefly mentioned, the present tense of verbs belonging to the third group is not always regular, and the root is not always stable either.

First example:

	DEVOIR	MUST / TO HAVE TO
	Radical : **doi/dev**	Root: **doi/dev**
	je d**ois**	I must
	tu d**ois**	you must
	il/elle/on d**oit**	he/she/it must
	nous dev**ons**	we must
	vous dev**ez**	you must
	ils/elles d**oivent**	they must

Second example:

ALLER	TO GO
Radical : **v** or **all**	Root: **v** or **all**
je **vais**	I go
tu **vas**	you go
il/elle/on **va**	he/she/it goes
nous all**ons**	we go
vous all**ez**	you go
ils/elles **vont**	they go

Third example:

FAIRE	TO DO / TO MAKE
Radical : **fai** or **f**	Root: **fai** or **f**
Je f**ais**	I make / do
Tu f**ais**	you make / do
Il/elle/on f**ait**	he/she/it makes / does
nous f**aisons**	you make / do
vous f**aites**	we make / do
Ils/elles f**ont**	they make / do

EXERCISES
EXERCICES

1) Find and use in context! (Find audio on page 14.)

Trouvez et utilisez en contexte !

In the first part of this exercise, you will hear a verb in its infinitive form. Listen carefully and match each verb to the corresponding picture. All the verbs belong to the first or second group and are, therefore, regular verbs. Put them in their infinitive form next to the pictures. *Dans la première partie de cet exercice, vous entendrez un verbe à sa forme infinitive. Écoutez attentivement et associez chaque verbe à l'image correspondante. Tous les verbes appartiennent au premier ou au deuxième groupe et sont donc des verbes réguliers. Mettez-les à leur forme infinitive à côté des images.*

First part of the exercise
Première partie de l'exercice

Then, in the second part, you will use the verbs you have listened to in context and conjugate them correctly in the present tense. *Ensuite, dans la deuxième partie, vous utiliserez les verbes que vous avez entendus en contexte et les conjuguerez correctement au présent.*

Second part
Deuxième partie

a) Vous _____ tous les jours pendant plus d'une heure à la piscine municipale. C'est assez impressionnant !

You swim at the local swimming pool every day for over an hour. It is quite impressive!

b) Je _____ presque tout par carte, car je n'aime pas avoir de l'argent en liquide dans mon portefeuille. Je me sens plus rassuré de cette manière.

I pay almost everything with my card because I do not like having cash in my wallet. I feel safer this way.

c) Les élèves _____ leurs erreurs avec une gomme quand ils se trompent.

The pupils erase their mistakes with an eraser when they make a mistake.

d) Nous _____ souvent pendant deux mois l'été, car nous avons trois mois de vacances au total. Généralement, nous aimons passer un mois dans les Alpes et un mois en Guadeloupe.

We often travel for two months in the summer because we have three months of holidays per year. Usually, we like to spend one month in the Alps and one month in Guadeloupe.

e) Toi, tu _____ avec lui et moi avec elle pour le cours de salsa. Nous ferons différemment pour le cours de rock.

For the salsa lesson, you will dance with him, and I will dance with her. We will do differently for the rock lesson.

f) Nous _____ des trous dans les murs de la maison pour pouvoir accrocher les toiles que nous avons achetées aux enchères.

We are drilling some holes in the house so that we can hang the paintings we bought at the auction.

ACTIVE AND PASSIVE VOICES
VOIX ACTIVE ET VOIX PASSIVE

THE CAT DRANK THE MILK.   **THE MILK WAS DRUNK.**

To conjugate a verb, we need a mood (**mode** in French) and a tense (**temps** in French). For personal moods, we also need a person. Finally, we use a voice. We will come back to tense and personal and impersonal moods later.

RECOGNIZING THE ACTIVE OR THE PASSIVE VOICE
RECONNAÎTRE LA VOIX ACTIVE OU LA VOIX PASSIVE

To recognize whether a sentence is written in the active or passive voice, you have to ask yourself the following question: is the subject the one who carries out the action set out by the verb?

If you answer **yes** to that question, the subject carries out the action set out by the verb, and the sentence is thus in the active voice. Remember: active refers to action, so the subject is the one doing it.

If you answer **no** to that question, then the subject is not the one carrying the action, and the sentence is thus in the passive voice. Remember: passive refers to the fact of undergoing the action.

For example:

Active voice: La souris *mange* le fromage.
The mouse eats the cheese.

Passive voice: Le fromage *est mangé* par la souris.
The cheese is eaten by the mouse.

Those sentences are very similar. The meaning is almost the same, except that the emphasis is put on a different thing. In the active voice, the **emphasis** is put on the subject "mouse" whereas in the passive voice, the emphasis is put on the cheese.

What does this mean concretely? The first sentence could be used to answer the question: **who** ate the cheese?

The second sentence could be used to answer the question: **where** is the cheese?

How to recognize whether a sentence is written in the active or passive voice?

a) First, you should locate the **main verb** of the sentence. As a mnemonic method, you can underline or highlight it.

b) Second, you should locate the **subject** that accompanies the verb.

c) Finally, you should ask yourself whether the subject **carries out** the action or **undergoes** it.

Let us apply this method to our example. Our first sentence was: **la souris mange le fromage**.

a) The verb is **mange** (eats).

b) Who eats? In our sentence, **"la souris"** *(the mouse)* **eats** the cheese.

c) Who is carrying out the action? The mouse.

What does the mouse eat? The cheese. This means that the cheese is the **"COD"** in this sentence.

COD means **"complément d'object direct"** *(direct object complement)*. In a sentence, if there is one, the COD can easily be recognized by asking the question "Whom?" or "What?"

For example:

L'investisseur achète des peintures
The investor buys paintings.

What does the investor buy? Paintings. Therefore, "paintings" is the COD in this sentence.
The sentence in the passive voice is written as such:

Des peintures sont achetées par l'investisseur.
Paintings are bought by the investor.

NOTE

Have you noticed the ending of the verb **acheter** *(to buy)* in the previous example in the passive voice? It is achet**ées**. Indeed, in the passive voice, you must make the verb **agree** with the subject. In this case, **peintures** is a **feminine** and **plural**.

Now let us analyze the second sentence.

What is the verb? **"est mangé"** is the verb.

Who/What is eaten? In our sentence, **"le fromage"** *(the cheese)* is eaten.

Who/what is carrying out the action? **"La souris"** eats the cheese. Therefore, the cheese **undergoes** the action of being eaten.

Therefore, the sentence is written in the passive voice.

As you may have already noticed, the COD of an active voice sentence **becomes the subject** in a sentence written in the passive voice. It is introduced by the preposition **"par"**. It then becomes what is known as the **agent**.

The agent indicates who/what is doing the action in a sentence written in the passive voice. **The agent is the one that is doing the action**.

Very rarely, you may see **"de"** instead of **"par"** in sentences written in the passive voice.

Example with par:

a) Active voice: **L'enfant utilise un ordinateur**.
The child uses a computer.

b) Passive voice: **L'ordinateur est utilisé par un enfant**.
The computer is used by a child.

Example with de:

a) Active voice: **Tous les étudiants détestent les pauses d'une heure**.
The students hate one-hour breaks.

b) Passive voice: **Les pauses d'une heure sont détestées de tous les étudiants**.
One-hour breaks are hated by all the students.

In the latter, **"par"** could also be used, but it does not sound as good. However, you should consider that **"de"** in passive voice sentences is an exception for now. You may build all your passive voice sentences with par.

SENTENCES WITHOUT AN AGENT
PHRASES SANS COMPLÉMENT D'AGENT

It is also possible that some sentences written in the passive voice do not have an agent. Knowing who or what is carrying out the action is not mandatory. There are various reasons for not mentioning the agent. For example: one may want to create some mystery. One may not know who or what carried out the action, or the agent may also be so evident that it thus becomes unnecessary to mention it.

For example:

a) Active voice: On a **attaqué** le piéton trois fois.
Someone attacked the pedestrian three times.

b) Passive voice: Le piéton **a été attaqué** trois fois.
The pedestrian was attacked three times.

Notice the **on** in the active voice sentence. When you want to convert a sentence from the passive voice to the active voice but do not know who carried out the action, you can often use **on** as the subject. It works in English in some cases too, for example:

a) Passive voice: **<u>On</u> ne doit pas manger de pain avec la soupe**.
   <u>*One*</u> *must not eat the bread with the soup.*

b) Active voice: **Le pain ne doit pas être mangé avec la soupe**.
   The bread must not be eaten with the soup.

THE VERBAL FORM
LA FORME VERBALE

When a sentence is written in the active voice, the verb is simple.

However, when a sentence is written in the passive voice, the auxiliary verb **être** is used + the past participle of the verb.

Do not worry; we will come back to those complicated terms later.

Also, when we convert a sentence from the active voice to the passive voice, the auxiliary verb **être** should be in the **same tense as the main verb** of the active voice sentence.

a) Active voice: Le médecin **découvrira** un traitement.
   The doctor will discover a treatment.

b) Passive voice: Un traitement **sera découvert** par le médecin.
   A treatment will be discovered by the doctor.

You do not know how to conjugate **être** in the future tense yet, but **sera** means *will be*.

NOTE

When you see the auxiliary verb **être** in a sentence, it **does not necessarily** mean that the sentence is written in the passive voice. Compound forms exist in many tenses. To be completely sure you are facing a passive voice sentence, **ask yourself the questions we saw previously**.

Il est sorti du trou.
He climbed out of the hole.

c) What is the main verb? **Sortir** (to come out).

d) Whom or what is carrying out the action? **IL**.

e) What or whom is undergoing the action?
Nobody / nothing.

It is a sentence written in the active voice. How would the sentence be written in the passive voice? Well, you **cannot**. Some sentences cannot be written in the passive voice.

ACTIVE VOICE OR PASSIVE VOICE?
VOIX ACTIVE OU VOIX PASSIVE ?

How to choose whether to write a sentence in the passive or active voice? We mentioned it briefly before. It depends on what you would like to put the emphasis on.

Second remark:

To convert a sentence written in the active voice into the passive voice, the sentence written in the active voice must have a COD!

For example:

Je pars à Paris demain.
I am going to Paris tomorrow.

There is no direct object in this sentence.
Therefore, you cannot put it in the passive voice.

Second example:

a) Active voice: **L'enfant a eu un cadeau**.
The child got a present.

b) Passive voice: **Un cadeau a été eu par l'enfant**.
A present was gotten by the child.

The passive voice in this example sounds terrible, both in French and English. Therefore, the active voice should be used.

EXERCISES
EXERCICES

1) Listen to each sentence in the active voice and write it in the passive voice.
(Find audio on page 14.)
Écoutez chaque phrase à la voix active et écrivez-la à la voix passive.

a) Le public applaudit les comédiens de la troupe de théâtre.
The public applauds the comedians of the drama company.

_____.

b) L'école primaire organisera une fête de fin d'année.
The primary school will organize an end of the year party.

_____.

c) On utilisera ce système informatique pendant plusieurs années à l'université.
We will use this IT system for several years at the university.

_____.

d) L'entreprise va construire des immeubles au bord de la mer.
The company will build buildings by the seaside.

_____.

e) On a accusé l'élève alors qu'il n'avait rien fait.
We have accused the pupil even though he had not done anything.

_____.

f) Les insectes et les oiseaux ont mangé toutes les tomates de mon jardin.
Insects and birds ate all the tomatoes in my garden.

_____.

g) Le nouveau président le nommera sûrement premier ministre.
The new president will probably apppoint him as prime minister.

_____.

h) Le maire a aménagé une nouvelle zone industrielle pour promouvoir l'emploi.
The mayor developed a new industrial zone to promote employment.

_____.

i) Le scientifique a découvert un médicament contre une maladie infectieuse.
The scientist has discovered a treatment against an infectious disease.

_____.

j) Une tempête explosive a surpris un groupe de randonneurs suisses et belges.
An explosive storm surprised a group of Swiss and Belgian hikers.

_____.

MOST USED TENSES
LES TEMPS LES PLUS UTILISÉS

In French, the three most frequently used tenses are le **présent** (the present tense), le **passé composé** (the perfect tense, also known as the compound past), and le **futur simple** *(the simple future)*.

Here is an example of a sentence written in the present tense, in the perfect tense, and the simple future tense.

> **a) Aujourd'hui, je me lève tôt, je mange une pomme et je bois du thé.**
> *Today, I wake up early, I eat an apple and I drink tea.*

> **b) Hier, je me suis levé tôt, j'ai mangé une pomme et j'ai bu du thé.**
> *Yesterday, I woke up early, I ate an apple and I drank tea.*

> **c) Demain, je me lèverai tôt, je mangerai une pomme et je boirai du thé.**
> *Tomorrow, I will wake up early, I will eat an apple and I will drink tea.*

We have already seen the present tense in the previous sections. Let us see how to build the perfect tense in French.

BASIC PRINCIPLES FOR THE FORMATION OF THE PERFECT
PRINCIPES DE BASES POUR LA FORMATION DU PASSÉ COMPOSÉ

The compound past or perfect is often used to replace the simple past in oral speech. The simple past is more complicated to build than the perfect tense and is more common in written French.

FUN FACT

French people sometimes use the simple past in oral speech as a joke to pretend they are members of the royalty or aristocracy.

In order to build a sentence in the perfect tense, you need to follow the following structure:

auxiliary **être** *(to be)* or **avoir** *(to have)* + past participle.

---

1) What is the perfect tense or compound past?

The perfect tense is used to talk about a brief event or action that took place in the past and is now finished. We can also describe it as being the past tense close to the present tense.

For example:

a) Hier, son ami lui a apporté des fleurs et du chocolat.
Yesterday, his/her friend brought him/her some flowers and chocolate.

Now, let us dive into the method to conjugate verbs in the perfect tense in more detail.

As you now know, we use either **être** or **avoir** to conjugate verbs in the perfect tense.

For example:

a) J'ai mangé.
I ate.

b) Tu es sorti hier.
You went out yesterday.

c) Il/elle/on a bu de l'eau.
He/she/it drank water.

d) Nous sommes allés marcher sur la plage.
We went to have a walk on the beach.

e) Vous avez appelé la police.
You called the police.

f) Ils/elles sont partis pour les États-Unis d'Amérique.
They left for the United States of America.

2) The past participle
Le participe passé

By now, you should understand what regular (first and second groups) and irregular verbs (third group) are.

The past participle of a verb is built depending on the verb group.

A quick reminder: verbs belonging to the first group are those ending in **er**. Verbs belonging to the second group are those ending in **ir** and whose endings are **issons** and **issez**, respectively for the first- and second-person pronouns. Verbs belonging to the third group are irregular, like **mordre** *(to bite)*.

How do you know whether a verb should be used with **être** or **avoir** to conjugate it in the perfect tense?

Avoir is the auxiliary that is the most used to conjugate verbs in the perfect tense. The auxiliary verb **être** is only used for over a dozen verbs.

Apart from reflexive verbs, also known as pronominal verbs, verbs that use the auxiliary verb **être** for their conjugation in the perfect tense are:

naître *(to be born)*	**monter** *(to go up)*
décéder *(to pass away)*	**descendre** *(to go down)*
mourir *(to die)*	**entrer** *(to enter)*
devenir *(to become)*	**sortir** *(to go out, to come out)*
aller *(to go)*	**arriver** *(to arrive)*
venir *(to come)*	**rester** *(to stay)*
retourner *(to go back, to return, to turn something over)*	**partir** *(to leave)*
tomber *(to fall)*	

Some of those verbs also have compounds forms, for example:

a) revenir *(to come back)*

b) rentrer *(to go home, to come in)*

These two verbs are based on **venir** and **entrer**.

All reflexive verbs should also be included in the list. Reflexive verbs are verbs that are used with reflexive pronouns, such as **"se," "me," "te," "se," "nous," "vous," "se,"** depending on the subject.

For example:

	S'APPELER	TO BE CALLED
	Radical : **appel**	Root: **appel**
	je **m'**appelle	I am called
	tu **t'**appelles	you are called
	il/elle/on **s'**appelle	he/she/it is called
	nous **nous** appelons	we are called
	vous **vous** appelez	you are called
	ils/elles **s'**appellent	they are called

2.1) Perfect tense of s'appeler:
S'appeler au passé composé:

je **me** suis appelé	I was called
tu **t'**es appelé(e)	you were called
il/elle/on **s'**est appelé(e)	he/she/it was called
nous **nous** sommes appelé(e)s	we were called
vous **vous** êtes appelé(e)s	you were called
ils/elles **se** sont appelé(e)s	they were called

2.2) Sortir in the perfect tense:

Sortir au passé composé:

SORTIR	TO GO OUT
Radical : **sor**	Root: **sor**
je suis sort**i(e)**	I went out
tu es sort**i(e)**	you went out
il/elle/on est sort**i(e)**	he/she/it went out
nous sommes sort**i(e)s**	we went out
vous êtes sort**i(e)s**	you went out
ils/elles sont sort**i(e)s**	they went out

However, if sortir is used with a COD, it is then conjugated with avoir in the perfect tense. When sortir is used with a COD, its meaning changes, which means to take something out.

For example:

a) Je sors les poubelles.
I take the trash out.

Conjugation of <u>sortir les poubelles</u> in the perfect tense with the verb <u>avoir</u>:

j'**ai sorti** les poubelles	I took the trash out.
tu **as sorti** les poubelles	you took the trash out.
il/elle/on **a sorti** les poubelles	he/she/it took the trash out.
nous **avons sorti** les poubelles	we took the trash out.
vous **avez sorti** les poubelles	you took the trash out.
ils/elles **ont sorti** les poubelles	they took the trash out.

3) The rules to make the verb agree with the subject or direct object

The rules to make the verb agree with the subject or direct object vary depending on which auxiliary verb is used to build the perfect tense of the verb.

You also have to check whether the verb is pronominal (also known as reflexive). If that is the case, you have to follow the rules related to reflexive verbs.

If the auxiliary verb used to build the perfect tense of the verb is **être**, the past participle must agree with the gender (masculine, feminine) and the number (singular, plural) of the subject.

For example:

> **a) Elles sont nées au mois de juillet, le même jour à la même heure**.
> *They (fem. pl.) were born in July, on the same day, at the same time.*

> **b) Il s'est lavé le visage avant de dormir.**
> *He washed his face before going to sleep.*

> **c) Nous sommes allés à Trois-Rivières l'année dernière.**
> *We went to Trois-Rivières last year.*

If the auxiliary verb used is **avoir**, the past participle must agree in gender and number with the COD (direct object complement) **only** if the COD is placed **before** the verb.

An example where the COD is placed after the verb, so the past participle does not need agree in gender and number with the COD:

a) Jean-Luc a sorti les fleurs. / *Jean-Luc took out the flowers.*

An example where the direct objects are placed before the verb and where the past participle thus needs to agree in gender and number with the COD:

b) Jean-Luc les a sorties. / *Jean-Luc took them out.*

Here, "les" refers to "fleurs" (flowers), which is feminine and plural. Here's another example:

a) Jean-Luc a sorti le linge. / *Jean-Luc took out the laundry.*

b) Jean-Luc l'a sorti. / *Jean-Luc took it out.*

Here, "l'a" refers to "linge" (laundry), which is masculine and singular.

Reflexive verbs (those with **"se"** before) always agree with the subject in gender and number, for example:

a) Marie-Pierre s'est levée soudainement.
Marie-Pierre suddenly stood up.

b) Jean-Claude et Alexandre se sont baignés dans le lac.
Jean-Claude and Alexandre swam in the lake.

IMPORTANT REMARK

The past participle never agrees in gender and number with an indirect object. It agrees with **DIRECT OBJECTS ONLY**.

For example:

Matthieu et Louis se sont parlé. / *Matthieu and Louis talked to each other.*

REMINDER

To determine whether an object is direct or indirect, ask yourself the question **qui** or **quoi** (whom or what). If you can answer that question with the object directly, then it is a direct object. However, if you have to ask yourself the question to whom or to what (**à qui** or **à quoi**), then it is an indirect object.

In our previous example:

Matthieu et Louis se sont parlé. / *Matthieu and Louis talked to each other.*

Matthieu and Louis talked **to whom**? Matthieu et Louis ont parlé À qui ? It is an **indirect** object complement (**complément d'objet indirect** or **COI** in French).

There are more advanced topics to cover regarding reflexive verbs, but we will come back to those issues in the section about reflexive verbs.

4) When to use the perfect tense?

The perfect tense is used to talk about brief **events or actions that ended in the recent past**.

Once again, there are always exceptions in French. Therefore, sometimes the perfect tense might be used to describe **repeated actions** or even **future actions**. There are similar uses in English.

Brief action that has now ended:

a) Il a réparé sa voiture.
   He fixed his car.

Repeated action:

b) Je me suis baigné trois fois dans ma piscine aujourd'hui.
   I swam in my pool three times today.

Future action:

c) Il a bientôt fini d'écrire son histoire.
   He is almost done writing his story
   (lit. He has almost finished writing his story).

EXERCISES
EXERCICES

1) Complétez les verbes proposés en dessous du tableau au présent et reliez les éléments selon le modèle.

Write the verbs in the present tense and connect them to the corresponding element according to the example.

Les lapins	se nourrissent	de carottes.
Les feuilles des arbres		la méchanceté.
Les jus de fruits		toujours trop lentement.
Les juristes		rapidement en automne.
Le public		mal au frigo.
Nous		au feu orange.
Je		les soignants.
Les voitures		les criminels.

Verbs à utiliser
Verbs to use

Vieillir *(to age / grow old)*, **punir** *(to punish)*, **jaunir** *(to turn yellow)*, **se nourrir** *(to feed on, to eat)*, **agir** *(to act)*, **haïr** *(to hate)*, **ralentir** *(to slow down)*, **applaudir** *(to applaude)*

CLASSIFICATION OF VERBS

CLASSIFICATION DES VERBES

TRANSITIVE AND INTRANSITIVE
TRANSITIFS ET INTRANSITIFS

TRANSITIVE VERBS
VERBES TRANSITIFS

Transitive verbs are verbs followed by an object complement, known as complément d'objet in French.

There are two types of object complements: direct object complement or indirect object complement.

1) Direct object complement
Complément d'objet direct

The direct object complement is also known as complément d'objet direct or COD for short in French. You are already familiar with the concept of COD, as it has been introduced in previous sections.

As a reminder, to find out whether a word or a group of words is a COD, you should ask the question, whom or what?

For example:

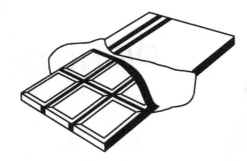

Nathan mange du chocolat.
Nathan eats chocolate.

The question: Nathan mange **quoi ? *What*** *does Nathan eat.*

The answer: Nathan mange **du chocolat**. / *Nathan eats **chocolate**.*

Therefore, **du chocolat** is the COD.

An example where there is no COD:

Claude nage.
Claude swims.

The question: Claude nage **quoi ? What** does Claude swim?

The answer: the syntax is **invalid**, and the sentence is therefore wrong.

There is no COD in the sentence.

2) Indirect Object Complement
Complément d'objet indirect

The indirect object complement, also known as **complément d'objet indirect** or **COI** in French, is a word or group of words that is connected to the verb with the help of a **preposition** to add meaning to the verb.

It is a complement, which means it **completes** the verb.

The questions you need to ask yourself to find out whether a sentence contains a COI or not are:

    a) à qui ? *(to whom?)* / **pour qui ?** *(for whom?)*

    b) à quoi ? *(to what?)* / **pour quoi ?** *(for what?)*

    c) de qui ? *(from whom?)*

    d) contre qui ? *(against whom?)*

    e) de quoi ? *(from what?)*

    f) contre quoi ? *(against what?)*

    g) sur quoi ? *(on what)*

Example:

Marc demande aux étudiants de se taire.
Marc asks the students to be quiet.

The question: **À qui** Marc demande de se taire ? / **Whom** does Marc ask to be quiet?

The answer: **aux** étudiants / **to the** students

Therefore, **aux étudiants** is the COI.

Another example:

L'écrivain pense à son livre.
The writer thinks about his book.

The question: **À quoi** pense l'écrivain ? / **What** does the writer think **about?**

The answer: **à** son livre / **about** his book

Therefore, **à son livre** is the COI.

3) Transitive-direct verbs
Verbes transitifs directs

Transitive-direct verbs are those which can **immediately** be followed by their object complement. In other words, they are verbs that are followed by a direct object complement (COD).

Example:

a) Le renard mange du poisson.
The fox eats some fish.

b) Le renard mange **quoi ?**
What *does the fox eat?*

c) Du poisson.
Some fish.

Therefore, the verb mange is transitive-direct in this sentence.

4) Transitive-indirect verbs
Verbes transitifs indirects

Transitive-indirect verbs are verbs followed by an indirect object complement (COI).

Example:

a) Je parle de mes voyages.
I talk about my trips.

b) The question: **De quoi** est-ce que je parle ?
What *do I talk **about?***

c) The answer: **De** mes voyages.
About *my trips.*

Therefore, the verb **parler**, in this context, is transitive-indirect.

5) Transitive-direct and transitive-indirect at the same time
Verbes transitifs directs et indirects en même temps

Some verbs can be both transitive-direct and transitive-indirect at the same time because they have **two objects**.

Example:

Ils enseignent la conjugaison française aux élèves.
They teach French conjugation to the students.

The question to find out what the direct object complement is:

a) Qu'enseignent-ils ?
***What** do they teach?*

b) The answer: **la conjugaison française.**
French conjugation.

Therefore, the direct object complement is **la conjugaison française**.

The question to find out what the indirect object complement is:

a) À qui enseignent-ils ?
***To whom** do they teach?*

b) Aux élèves.
***To** the students.*

Therefore, the indirect object complement is **aux élèves**. When there is a second complement in a sentence, we call it the second object complement, known as **complément d'objet second** or *COS* in French.

Therefore, the verb has two objects, one direct and one indirect, and is thus both transitive-direct and transitive-indirect.

Such verbs are called double transitive verbs, or **verbes transitifs doubles** in French.

INTRANSITIVE VERBS
VERBES INTRANSITIFS

Intransitive verbs are verbs **not** followed by an object complement, whether it be direct or indirect. They are often followed by an *adverbial phrase of place or time.*

a) An adverbial phrase of place is called a **complément circonstantiel de lieu** in French.

b) An adverbial phrase of time is called a **complément circonstantiel de temps** in French.

A sentence can have **several** adverbial phrases, for example:

a) Il est arrivé chez moi à huit heures en voiture.
He arrived at my house at eight o'clock by car.

What are the adverbial phrases of place and time in this sentence?

If you can answer to the question **"où"** / *"where"*, then the answer is probably the *adverbial phrase of place:*

a) Où est-il arrivé ? **Chez** moi. / **Where** *did he arrive?* **At** *my house.*

Therefore, **chez moi** is the adverbial phrase of place.

If you can answer to the question "**quand**" / *"when"*, then the answer is probably the *adverbial phrase of time.*

b) Quand est-il arrivé ? **À** huit heures. / **When** *did he arrive?* **At** *eight o'clock.*

Therefore, **à huit heures** is the adverbial phrase of time.

In our sentence, we also have an oddity: by car.

By car is the answer to the question:

c) Comment est-il arrivé ? **En** voiture. / **How** *did he arrive?* **By** *car.*

It is called *adverbial phrase of means.*

They are easy to recognize in the sense that you can usually remove them from the sentence without altering its main meaning.

For example:

a) J'ai croisé un ami à la banque.
I bumped into a friend at the bank.

If you remove the adverbial phrase of place *at the bank*, the sentence is still correct, and its original meaning is only slightly altered:

b) J'ai croisé un ami.
I bumped into a friend.

ADVANCED USAGE

Adverbial phrases can have different grammatical natures. They can be adverbs, nouns, pronouns, or even infinitive verbs.

Besides, some adverbial phrases cannot be removed from their sentence and are called essential complements because, without them, the sentence loses its complete meaning. This is mostly the case for prices, weights, or distances.

For example:

a) Cette voiture coûte 30 000 euros.
This car costs 30,000 euros.

b) Le bébé avait un poids de 3,6 kg à la naissance.
The baby had a weight of 3.6 kg at birth.

However, all these edge cases are out of scope for this book. Remember the questions used to identify the COD and COI in a sentence, and you should be just fine.

INTRANSITIVE USAGE OF TRANSITIVE VERBS
EMPLOI INTRANSITIF DES VERBES TRANSITIFS

Some transitive verbs may be used without their object complement. However, a context is **absolutely necessary** in this case, and it does **not** work for all verbs.

Examples of transitive verbs that can be used as intransitive verbs:

First example:

a) Transitive: **Annabelle range sa chambre**.
Literally translated as *Annabelle tidies her room.*
Better translation: *Annabelle is tidying her room.*

b) Intransitive: **Annabelle range**.
Literally translated as *Annabelle tidies.*
Better translation: *Annabelle is tidying.*

Second example:

a) Transitive: **Claudine pense au travail**.
Claudine thinks about work.

b) Intransitive: **Claudine pense**.
Claudine thinks or Claudine is thinking.

EXERCISES
EXERCICES

1) Listen and indicate whether the verb in the sentence is a transitive-direct, transitive-indirect or intransitive.

Écoutez et indiquez si le verbe de la phrase est un verbe transitif direct, transitif indirect ou intransitif.

a) J'ai besoin d'une voiture pour le travail.
I need a car for work.

_____ .

b) Nous ferons beaucoup de golf à partir du mois de mars.
We will play a lot of golf starting in March.

_____ .

c) Mes chats ont joué à la balle toute la journée.
My cats played ball all day long.

_____ .

d) Ma grand-mère va regarder les informations à la télévision dans une heure.
My grandmother is going to watch the news on television in an hour.

_____ .

e) Je rêve de partir en Martinique.
I dream of going to Martinique.

_____ .

f) Les chanteuses ont été applaudies par le public.
The singers (fem.) were applauded by the public.

_____ .

g) Mes enfants ne m'ont jamais obéi.
My children have never obeyed me.

_____.

h) Le petit garçon a été consolé par le docteur.
The little boy was comforted by the doctor.

_____.

i) Les hommes politiques répondent aux critiques de manière agressive.
Politicians reply to criticism aggressively.

_____.

j) Une personne m'a souri dans le métro hier.
A person smiled at me in the subway yesterday.

_____.

k) D'où ont été importés ces avocats ?
Where were these avocados imported from?

_____.

l) Mon ami a commercialisé un nouveau concept.
My friend has commercialized a new concept.

_____.

m) Mes chiens ont volé les carottes de mes lapins.
My dogs stole the carrots from my rabbits.

_____.

n) Mon fils a cassé ma console de jeu.
My son broke my video game console.

_____.

o) La petite abeille est adorable.
The little bee is adorable.

_____.

p) La planète Mercure a été prise en photo par le scientifique.
The planet Mercury was taken in pictures by the scientist.

_____.

q) Il y a des monstres et des sorcières dans les films d'horreur.
There are monsters and witches in horror movies.

_____.

r) Ce roman a été écrit par un enfant.
This novel was written by a child.

_____.

s) Ils ont raconté une histoire intéressante à la radio.
They told an interesting story on the radio.

_____.

t) Je vais te cuisiner un bon repas ce soir.
I will cook a nice little dish for you tonight.

_____.

IMPERSONAL
IMPERSONNELS

PERSONAL VERBS
VERBES PERSONNELS

This is an easy category. Personal verbs are verbs that can be conjugated with several persons, that is with *je*, *tu*, *il/elle/on*, *nous*, *vous*, and *ils/elles*.

You can say:

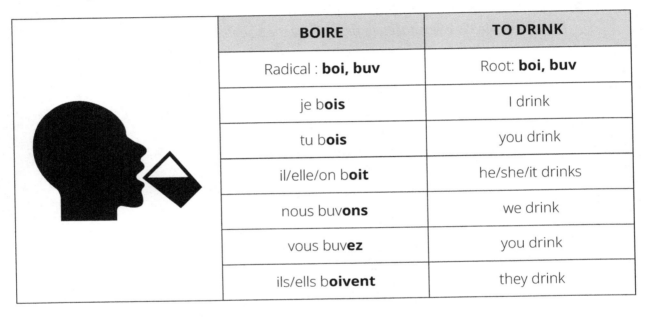

BOIRE	TO DRINK
Radical : **boi, buv**	Root: **boi, buv**
je b**ois**	I drink
tu b**ois**	you drink
il/elle/on b**oit**	he/she/it drinks
nous buv**ons**	we drink
vous buv**ez**	you drink
ils/ells b**oivent**	they drink

However, you cannot say: I rain, you rain, he/she/it rains, etc. Personal verbs are verbs that can be conjugated with all persons.

IMPERSONAL VERBS
VERBES IMPERSONNELS

Impersonal verbs are verbs that **cannot** be conjugated with all persons. They can be only conjugated with the third person singular: **il**.

In this context, **il** does not mean or refer to anything. We call it the *apparent subject* because it appears as and serves the function of the subject in the sentence.

In contrast, in a sentence with a personal verb such as **"Louis mange une pomme"**, *Louis* is called the *real subject* because Louis refers to an actual, real person.

There are different categories of impersonal verbs. Some of them are defined as strictly or essentially impersonal, or **strictement impersonnels** in French.

Some other verbs have an impersonal structure in their pronominal form. We will come back to this particular point later, so do not fear the scary words.

1) Essentially impersonal verbs
Verbes strictement impersonnels

Logically, essentially impersonal verbs are verbs that could not accept any subject other than **il**. Many of the verbs falling into this category can be compared to their counterparts in English.

1.1) Describing a meteorological state:

The first category of essentially impersonal verbs are verbs that describe a meteorological state,

For example:

a) Il pleut beaucoup à Londres.
   It rains a lot in London.

b) Il neige tous les hivers en Suisse.
   It snows every winter in Switzerland.

c) Il y a beaucoup de vent en Irlande.
It is very windy in Ireland.

d) Il grêle souvent quand il y a une tempête à Montréal.
It often hails when there is a storm in Montreal.

In these examples, you can see that **il** does not refer to a real or particular subject. The sentences written in English use it in the same way. **It** serves the same purpose and function as **il** in all those sentences. French might not be that complicated after all, right?

1.2) Describing an obligation, a necessity, or some advice:

Another essentially impersonal verb is **falloir** which roughly translates as to be **obligatory/necessary/preferable to** (do something).

For example:

a) Obligation / Obligation:

Il faut payer avant de partir du restaurant.
*Paying is an **obligation** before leaving the restaurant.*

b) Nécessité / Necessity:

Il faut des œufs pour faire une omelette.
*Eggs are **necessary** to make an omelette.*

c) Conseil / Advice:

Il faut faire attention aux voitures avant de traverser la route.

*It is **preferable** to watch out for cars before crossing the road.*

1.3) Describing what is enough:

One uses the impersonal verb **suffire de** to express what is enough, which roughly translates as *only needs to.*

For example:

a) Il suffit de fermer la porte pour que la pièce se réchauffe.
*One **only needs to** close the door for the room to warm up.*

2) Verbs which may have an impersonal structure
Verbes qui peuvent avoir une tournure impersonnelle

Some verbs may have an impersonal structure:

être *(to be)*

avoir *(to have)*

faire *(to do / to make)*

valoir *(to cost / to be worth)*

rester *(to stay / to remain)*

manquer *(to lack)*

arriver *(to arrive)*

paraître *(to appear / to seem / to look)*

sembler *(to seem / to look / to seem to be)*

résulter *(to result in)*

2.1) Être

Être can be used as an impersonal verb in expressions such as:

Il est préférable de bien dormir avant de conduire.
Having a good night of sleep is preferable before driving.

Literally, the sentence would be translated as: **It is** preferable to sleep well before driving.

2.2) Avoir

Avoir is used as an impersonal verb when *describing* things, people, or animals which or who exist. It works in a similar way as in English, and you should be familiar with this structure and understand it well.

Example:

Il y a beaucoup de chats dans le voisinage.
There are many cats in the neighborhood.

Il y a trop de beurre sur ma tartine de pain.
There is too much butter on my toasted bread.

NOTE

In English, the structure is *"there is"* or *"there are"* but in French, there is no difference between singular and plural since impersonal verbs can only be used with the third personal singular **"il"**.

2.3) Faire

Faire can be used as an impersonal verb to *describe the climate* or certain related things like the temperature.

For example:

a) Il fait froid en Sibérie.
It is cold in Siberia.

b) Il fait chaud à Chypre.
It is hot in Cyprus.

c) Il fait beau aujourd'hui.
The weather is nice today.

2.4) Valoir

Valoir can be used as an impersonal verb to describe something better or preferable in the expression "**il vaut mieux**" which could be translated as *"it is better to"*.

For example:

a) Il vaut mieux se protéger les yeux et porter des lunettes de soleil en été.
It is better to protect one's eyes and wear sunglasses in summer.

b) Il vaut mieux être respectueux et professionnel au travail.
It is better to be respectful and professional at work.

2.5) Rester

Rester can be used as an impersonal verb to describe *something that is left.*

For example:

a) Il reste deux oranges seulement.
*There are only two oranges **left**.*

2.6) Manquer

Manquer can be used as an impersonal verb to describe something something that is lacking, but is necessary in order to carry out something.

For example:

Il manque deux œufs pour faire la tarte. / *Two more eggs are **required** to bake the pie.*

It literally means: Two eggs are lacking to bake the pie.

2.7) Arriver

Arriver can be used as an impersonal verb to *describe an event*.

For example:

a) Il **est arrivé** un accident.
*An accident **happened.***

2.8) Paraître

Paraître can be used as an impersonal verb to describe something one has heard.

For example:

> **a) Il paraît** que tu déménages la semaine prochaine.
> ***I have heard*** *that you are moving next week.*

Literally, it translates as: it seems/appears like you are moving next week.

2.9) Sembler que

Sembler que is used as an impersonal verb to describe *something uncertain*.

For example:

> **a) Il semble** qu'il fasse plus chaud aujourd'hui qu'hier.
> ***It seems like*** *it is hotter today than yesterday.*

2.10) Résulter

Résulter is used as an impersonal verb to *describe a consequence*.

For example:

> **a)** Tout le monde parle en même temps. Cela **résulte en** un vacarme assourdissant.
> *Everybody is speaking at the same time. It **results in** a deafening noise.*

3) Verbs which have an impersonal structure in their pronominal form
Verbes à tournure impersonnelle dans leur forme pronominale

We will come back to what the pronominal form of a verb is later. For now, you just need to know that a *reflexive verb* is a verb with **"se"** like **"s'appeler"**, like in **"Je m'appelle Pierre"**. You should now have a good understanding of what an impersonal verb is. Therefore, you can learn the structures and use them already.

Examples of verbs that have an impersonal structure in their pronominal form are: **s'agir de** *(to be a matter of something)*, **s'avérer** *(to turn out to be)*, **se produire** *(to happen / to occur)*, and **se pouvoir** *(may / might / to be possible)*.

3.1) S'agir

S'agir is used to introduce something or someone.

Example:

> **a)** Il **s'agit de** la voiture blanche = C'est la voiture blanche.
> ***It is** the white car.*

 It can be an answer when asked to clarify. For example, we know that Paul has three cars, you can listen to the following dialogue:

a) Pierre: Tu peux me prêter une voiture ? / *Can you lend me a car?*

b) Paul: Oui, je vais te prêter ma préférée. / *Yes, I will lend you my favorite one.*

a) Pierre: De laquelle **s'agit-il ?** / *Which one **is it**?*

b) Paul: **Il s'agit** de la rouge. / ***It is** the red one.*

3.2) S'avérer

S'avérer is used to express an observation.

For example:

a) Il s'avère qu'il pleut beaucoup.
It turns out to be raining a lot.

3.3) Se produire

Se produire is used to describe an event.

For example:

a) Il s'est produit une catastrophe.
A catastrophe happened.

3.4) Se pouvoir que

Se pouvoir que is used to talk about a possibility.

For example:

a) Il se peut que mon chat se cache.
My cat may be hiding.

EXERCISES
EXERCICES

1) Fill in the gaps with the correct options.

Remplissez les trous avec les options correctes.

a) Quand _____, _____ un parapluie.

When it rains, an umbrella is required.

· il neige   · il pleut   · il faut   · il vente

b) _____ beaucoup de courage pour faire du saut à l'élastique.

Courage is enough to go bungee jumping.

· Il grêle   · Il s'agit de   · Il suffit de   · Il s'avère que

c) _____ seulement quatre bananes au frigo.
There are only four bananas left in the fridge.

- Il faut   • Il semble que   • Il y a   • Il reste

d) _____ que ta collègue est partie à la retraite.
I've heard that your colleague had retired.

- Il manque   • Il vaut mieux   • Il est préférable   • Il paraît

e) Quand c'est l'hiver, _____ mettre des chaussettes chaudes.
In winter, it is better to put on warm socks.

- il pleut   • il vaut mieux   • il suffit de   • il y a

f) Quand _____ beau, _____ des abeilles dehors.
When the weather is nice, there are bees outside.

· il faut   · il fait   · il y a   · il résulte

REFLEXIVE VERBS
LES VERBES RÉFLÉCHIS

A reflexive verb is a verb that is *preceded by a personal pronoun* we call reflexive, or **réfléchi** in French.

You already know a reflexive verb (also known as pronominal verb): **s'appeler**.

Je m'appelle is reflexive because the *"m"* means *myself*. Literally, **"je m'appelle"** is translated as *"I call myself"*.

When you see **"se"** before a verb, it means it is a pronominal or reflexive verb.

The reflexive personal pronouns are:

m' / me	myself
t' / te	yourself
s' / se	himself/herself/itself
nous	ourselves
vous	yourselves
s' / se	themselves

You have seen the conjugation of the verb **s'appeler** in the present, the perfect tense, and the simple future in the previous sections.

We will show you another example with the verb to **wash oneself**:

	SE LAVER	TO WASH ONESELF
	Radical : **lav**	Root: **lav**
	je **me** lave	I wash myself
	tu **te** laves	you wash yourself
	il elle on **se** lave	he washes himself she washes herself it washes itself
	nous **nous** lavons	we wash ourselves
	vous **vous** lavez	you wash yourselves
	ils/elles **se** lavent	they wash themselves

The verb is preceded by a double pronoun, the subject, e.g., "**je**" (*I*), and the reflexive pronoun, e.g., "me" (myself).

QUESTION

Do you notice anything about the function of the reflexive pronoun in our sentence?

TIP

Ask yourself the question, "what/whom do I wash?"

Indeed, the reflexive pronoun in these cases is the *direct object complement!* As you can see, the direct object complement can sometimes be before the verb.

You should already know that by now, since you have seen it with the verb **"s'appeler"** in previous sections, but when we conjugate a pronominal verb in the perfect tense, we use the auxiliary verb **être**, and the past participle **should agree** with the *direct object complement* (the reflexive pronoun in the case of pronominal verbs) when it is placed before the verb.

Conjugation of <u>se laver</u> in the perfect tense:

SE LAVER	TO WASH ONESELF
Radical : **se lav**	Root: **se lav**
je **me** suis lavé(e)	I washed myself
tu **t'**es lavé(e)	you washed yourself
il elle on **s'**est lavé(e)	he washed himself she washed herself it washed itself
nous **nous** sommes lavé(e)s	we washed ourselves
vous **vous** êtes lavé(e)s	you washed yourselves
ils/elles **se** sont lavé(e)s	they washed themselves

Note that some people may make the past participle agree with **"on"** and add an **"s"** because **"on"** usually refers to a group of people. However, this is rarely acceptable and is mostly done as a figure of speech by writers. The correct way is to conjugate **"on"** as a *third person singular,* which is precisely what it is.

RECIPROCAL VERBS
VERBES RÉCIPROQUES

A pronominal verb is classified as reciprocal when it refers to an action carried out by several subjects onto each other. Each of them is thus a receiver of the action.

For example:

a) Les amis **s'**entraident.
*Friends help **each other**.*

b) Les parents de Jeanne **s'**aiment.
*Jeanne's parents love **each other**.*

Reciprocal verbs can only be used in their plural form and expressions like **l'un l'autre** *(each other)*, **les uns les autres** *(each other, more than two people)* may be added after. For example, with our previous examples:

a) Les amis s'entraident les uns les autres.

b) Les parents de Jeanne s'aiment l'un l'autre.

The meaning of these two sentences remains unaltered.

PRONOMINAL VERBS WITH A PASSIVE MEANING
VERBES PRONOMINAUX DE SENS PASSIF

Those verbs are usually used in the third person singular, and it is usually challenging to tell what or who carries out the action.

For example:

a) L'odeur des plats **se** sent dans tout le voisinage.
The aroma of the dishes can be smelled in the whole neighborhood.

b) La musique **s'**entend dans toute l'école.
   The music can be heard in the whole school.

c) Mon livre **se** vend bien.
   My book sells well.

EXERCISES
EXERCICES

 1) The audio will describe Marie-Louise's daily routine. Listen and fill in the gaps with the correct form of the pronominal verb:

L'audio décrira la routine quotidienne de Marie-Louise. Écoutez et remplissez les trous avec la forme correcte du verbe pronominal:

You may use a dictionary for this exercise. However, all the verbs used in this exercise are very common, and you should be familiar with most of them already.

a) Marie-Louise _____ tous les matins à six heures.
Marie-Louise wakes up every morning at six o'clock.

b) Elle _____ immédiatement.
She gets up immediately.

c) Elle doit _____ car elle n'a pas beaucoup de temps avant d'aller au travail.

She has to hurry up because she does not have much time before going to work.

d) Son fils doit _____ tout seul le midi, car elle n'a pas de pause.

Her son must have a walk alone during lunch break because she does not have one herself.

e) Elle ne _____ pas pour lui, car il a déjà quinze ans.

She is not worried about him because he is fifteen already.

COPULAR VERBS

VERBES À COPULES

When a person carries out an action, the verb is known as an **action verb**.

For example:

a) Il mange de la salade.
He eats salad.

When a person does not carry out an action, the verb is known as a **state verb**, also known as **copular verb** or **attributive verb**. Some examples of copular verbs are **être** *(to be)*, **demeurer** *(to remain / to keep / to stay)*, **paraître** *(to seem)*, **passer pour** *(to look like)*, **sembler** *(to seem)*, **rester** *(to remain / to stay)*, **avoir l'air** *(to look like / to seem)*.

PURPOSE
OBJECTIF

Usually, a copular verb introduces a *predicative of the subject* which, in simple terms, means something that *complements the subject* of the sentence by *completing its meaning*.

The predicative of the subject can either be a noun, an adjective, a nominal group, or a proposition.

For example:

a) L'élève semblait énervé.

The student seemed annoyed.

Semblait is a **state verb**, it describes a state.

Énervé is a *verbal adjective* and is the *predicative of the subject* "élève", meaning énervé completes the meaning of the latter.

TIP

To check if a verb is a copular verb, we can replace the verb with **être** *(to be).* If the sentence's meaning *is not or only slightly altered,* the verb is a copular one.

NOTE

Énerve is a verbal adjective in French because it is the past participle of the verb **"énerver"** *(to annoy / to get on somebody's nerves).* It is, therefore, a conjugated form of the verb énerver, which acts as an adjective. In English, a verbal adjective would be *annoying,* for example, because it is a conjugated form of the verb to *annoy.* In the sentence "He is annoying his siblings", *annoying* is a valid form.

EXERCISES
EXERCICES

1) After each sentence, you can pause the audio and indicate whether the verb is an action or an attributive verb.

Après chaque phrase, vous pouvez mettre en pause l'audio et indiquer si le verbe est un verbe d'action ou un verbe attributif.

a) Raymond a arrosé son cactus aujourd'hui.
   Raymond watered his cactus today.

_____ .

b) L'équipe de sauveteurs est épuisée.
   The lifeguard team is exhausted.

_____ .

c) Ma grand-mère semble très amoureuse de mon grand-père.
My grandmother seems very in love with my grandfather.

_____.

d) Le joueur de golf paraît fatigué.
The golf player looks exhausted.

_____.

e) Mes parents font la vaisselle.
My parents are washing the dishes.

_____.

AUXILIARY VERBS

VERBES AUXILIAIRES

You already know a lot about auxiliary verbs. Indeed, you already know what auxiliary verbs are, which verbs are auxiliary verbs, and how to use them. In this section, thanks to the knowledge you have acquired until now, you will be able to understand them in depth. Mastering auxiliary verbs will allow you to move on to the next levels confidently, that is, B1 and B2, on the Common European Framework of Reference for Languages (CEFR Levels).

CHOOSING THE RIGHT AUXILIARY VERB
CHOISIR LE VERBE AUXILIAIRE CORRECT

Compound tenses are formed using the *conjugated auxiliary verb and the past participle of the verb* we are conjugating.

Great, you now know what a direct object complement is, so you are ready to learn a new rule:

When using the auxiliary verb **avoir** *(to have)*, the past participle agrees with the direct object complement (*COD* in French) if, and only if, there is one, and if it is placed before the verb in the sentence.

For example:

> **a) J'ai mangé des pommes**.
>> *I ate apples.*

But:

> **b)** Les pommes que j'ai mang**ées**.
>> *The apples that I ate.*

Les pommes is before the verb and is the direct object complement (What did I eat? The apples); therefore, the verb **manger** agrees with apples in gender and in number. **Pomme** is feminine (its article is **la**), and there are several apples, so you take the radical as usual, **mang**, and add **ées** to it, **é** for the past participle, **e** for the feminine, and **s** for the plural form.

You should already be familiar with this at this stage. Make sure to go back to previous sections if some points are unclear, as it is important to build on solid foundations.

You now know what transitive verbs (those that can have a direct or indirect object complement after them) are. Transitive verbs **are always conjugated with the auxiliary verb avoir** in their compound tenses.

For example:

a) Je fais du thé.
I am making some tea.

b) J'**ai** fait du thé.
I made some tea.

It works in a similar way in English in this case since the auxiliary verb for those verbs is also have in compound tenses, for example: I **have** made tea.

You also know what pronominal, or reflexive, verbs are now. **All pronominal verbs** (which have **se** in front of them) **are conjugated with the auxiliary verb être**.

For example:

a) Je me lave.
I wash myself.

b) Je me **suis** lavé.
I washed myself.

a) Je m'assois.
I sit.

b) Je me **suis** assise.
I sat.

Some intransitive verbs (those which have no direct or indirect object complement) are *conjugated using the auxiliary verb être* in their compound forms. Those verbs usually express movement or transformation (evolution).

For example (movement):

    a) Je vais.
      I go.

    b) Je **suis** allé.
      I went.

    c) Je pars.
      I leave.

    d) Je **suis** parti.
      I left.

Second example (transformation):

    a) Je deviens.
      I become.

    b) Je **suis** devenu.
      I became.

Finally, sentences constructed **in the passive voice are always conjugated with the auxiliary verb être.**

Exceptions:

You do not need to know them at this point in your learning journey, but you should know some exceptions exist as you may encounter them.

There are exceptions as some verbs that express movement are conjugated with the auxiliary verb **avoir** in their compound forms when they are *used in a transitive way*. They are conjugated with the auxiliary verb *être* in their intransitive forms.

Some verbs that express change and are normally conjugated with the auxiliary verb **avoir** to **emphasize the change** itself, can be conjugated with the auxiliary verb *être* to **emphasize the result of the change** rather than the change itself.

And now, an example with the word... <u>change</u> itself:

    a) Je change.
      I change.

b) Je **suis** changé.

I changed.

c) Je **serai** changé.

I will have changed.

In the previous examples, we focus on the change, the process of changing, by using the auxiliary verb **être** in the compound tenses.

a) Je change.

I change.

b) J'**ai** changé.

I changed.

c) J'**aurai** changé.

I will have changed.

In the previous examples, we focus on the result. When we say, **"J'ai changé"**, we focus on the "new me", on the fact that I am not who I used to be anymore.

Example dialogue:

a) Micheline: J'aime beaucoup le sport.

I like sports a lot.

b) Emmannuel: Tu devrais aller à la gym l'année prochaine.

You should go to the gym next year.

c) Micheline: Qui sait ? J'aurai peut-être changé d'ici là.

Who knows? I may have changed by then.

EXERCISES
EXERCICES

1) Underline the right auxiliary verb.

Soulignez le verbe auxiliaire correct.

   a) Mes parents **sont / ont** allés au cinéma hier soir.

   My parents went to the cinema yesterday night.

   b) Mes amis et moi **avons / sommes** rentrés tôt cet après-midi.

   My friends and I came home early this afternoon.

   c) Le vent **est / a** fait tomber un arbre dans la nuit.

   The wind made a tree fall down in the night.

   d) Elle **est / a** participé à une compétition de peinture.

   She participated in a painting competition.

   e) Son devoir **a / est** dû depuis plus d'une semaine.

   His/Her homework is over a week late.

SEMI-AUXILIARY VERBS
VERBES SEMI-AUXILIAIRES

The two auxiliary verbs être and **avoir** are *not only* auxiliary verbs. **They are also verbs in their own right**.

Être can serve different functions, which we have seen so far:

   a) Impersonal verb: Il **est** midi.
   It is midday.

   b) Intransitive in the sense of "to exist": **Être**, ou ne pas **être**.
   To be, or not to be.

   c) To indicate location: Je **suis** à Paris.
   I am in Paris.

   d) As an attributive: Nous **sommes** fatigués.
   We are tired.

   e) To express passive voice: Les patates **sont** mangées par les insectes.
   The potatoes are eaten by insects.

   f) As an auxiliary verb: Je suis rentré chez moi.
   I came home.

Avoir can also serve several functions:

   a) To express possession: Mes amis ont une voiture.
   My friends have a car.

   b) To express a sensation: J'ai faim.
   I am hungry.

   c) As an auxiliary verb: J'ai bien dormi hier soir.
   I slept well last night.

Additionally, there are other common and important semi-auxiliary verbs in French, such as **"pouvoir"** (to be able to) and **"vouloir"** (to want).

Pouvoir (to be able to):

a) To express ability or possibility:

Je peux parler français.
I can speak French.

b) To make a request or ask for permission:

Est-ce que je peux emprunter votre stylo ?
Can I borrow your pen?

Examples:

a) Je peux venir demain.
I can come tomorrow.

b) Tu peux m'aider avec mes devoirs ?
Can you help me with my homework?

Vouloir (to want):

a) To express desire or intention:

Je veux acheter ce livre.
I want to buy this book.

b) To make a request or ask for something:

Je veux un café, s'il vous plaît.
I want a coffee, please.

Examples:

a) Je veux partir en vacances.
I want to go on vacation.

b) Il veut rencontrer le directeur.
He wants to meet the manager.

SEMI-AUXILIARY VERBS
VERBES SEMI-AUXILIAIRES

The semi-auxiliary verbs are: **aller** *(to go)*, **venir** *(to come)*, **devoir** *(must)*, **pouvoir** *(can)*, **savoir** *(to know)*, **vouloir** *(to want)*, **faire** *(to do / to make)*.

Semi-auxiliary verbs are verbs that *introduce a new subtlety or nuance to the action* when combined with another verb in the infinitive form.

What do you notice about the following examples:

a) Ils finissent leurs devoirs.
They finish their homework.

b) Ils **doivent** finir leurs devoirs.
*They **must** finish their homework.*

You may not be very familiar with the conjugation of irregular verbs yet. So far, you should just know how to recognize them. In this case, did you recognize that **doivent** is the conjugated form of **devoir** with the third person plural in the present tense? If you did, great! If not, don't worry, with exposure and practice exercises in this book, you'll become accustomed to them over time.

In this example, **"doivent"** adds a nuance to the sentence because we now know explicitly that they must finish their homework, whereas it was rather implicit in the first sentence, in the sense that it could have been implied in context, in a dialogue.

For example:

a) Anna: Tu viens manger ?
Are you coming to eat?

b) Jean: Je finis mes devoirs.
I am finishing my homework.

c) Anna: Ok, pas de problème.
Ok, no problem.

In this context, we understand that Jean must finish his homework even if he does not say it *explicitly*. With the help of the semi-auxiliary verb devoir, we can **add a nuance** to this dialogue:

a) Anna: Tu viens manger ?
Are you coming to eat?

b) Jean: Je **dois** finir mes devoirs.
I must finish my homework.

c) Anna: Ok, pas de problème.
Ok, no problem.

We now understand Jean must finish his homework before going to eat. He has no choice.

Let us study another example with **faire**.

a) J'ausculte mon chat.
I examine my cat.

b) Je **fais** ausculter mon chat par le vétérinaire.
*I **make** the veterinarian examine my cat.*

1) Aller + infinitive form of a verb
Aller + verbe à l'infinitif

Near future is expressed using **aller** + infinitive form of a verb. It works a bit like in English with "to be going to do something". You should learn this form by heart.

Example:

a) Je mange une orange.
I eat an orange.

b) Je **vais** manger une orange.
*I **am going to** eat an orange.*

2) Venir de + infinitive form of a verb

Venir de + verbe à l'infinitif

To express something that happened in the recent past, **venir de** + infinitive form of a verb is used. You should also learn this form by heart, as it is also extremely common and used all the time.

For example:

a) Je **mange** une poire.
  I eat a pear.

b) Je **viens de** manger une poire.
  *I **just** ate a pear.*

If you cannot remember all the verbs and forms mentioned in this section, try to memorize at least how to perfectly use **aller** and **venir** as they are very useful in daily life, and one could say they are even *omnipresent* in daily speech.

EXERCISES
EXERCICES

1) Fill in the gaps with the correct verb.

Remplir les trous avec le verbe correct.

Do not worry if you do not get all of them right.

a) Je _____ de me lever.
 I just woke up.

b) Il _____ savoir tout cela pour réussir son examen.
 He must know all this to pass his exam.

c) Ils _____ de finir leur repas.
 They just finished their meal.

d) On _____ boire beaucoup d'eau quand on fait de l'exercice.
 One must drink a lot of water when exercising.

e) Je _____ faire mes devoirs à mon frère.
 I make my brother do my homework.

f) Nous _____ réparer la voiture.
 We are going to fix the car.

PHRASAL VERBS
LES LOCUTIONS VERBALES

In this chapter, you are going to learn about French phrasal verbs. Phrasal verbs serve similar purposes and functions in French and English, but not entirely. Phrasal verbs are also known as verbal expressions.

You may be interested in learning more about them in your learning journey. If you are interested in knowing more at some point, know that they are also called: **expressions idiomatiques** (idiomatic expressions), **expressions imagées** (expressions full of imagery), **"phrases toutes faites"** (premade phrases), etc., to mention **some of them**.

WHAT IS A LOCUTION VERBALE?

It is a group of words constituting a fixed phrase, or fixed syntactic unit, or fixed syntagma (arrangement/constitution). That group of words has the same grammatical characteristics as a single word.

Locutions verbales represent an arbitrary association of words, which means a synchronically unpredictable sequence when compared with syntactic and semantic rules.

AAAAAAHHHH!!!

Did that sound scary? Do not fear linguistic jargon. All of this means, in simple terms, that a **locution verbale is a group of words that consists of a verb followed by one or several words, and that group of words expresses an idea and plays the role of a verb**.

Example of French verbal expressions:

a) Se jeter à l'eau

"**Se jeter à l'eau**" literally means to throw oneself in the water. However, you can probably imagine that most of the time, when you hear that verbal expression in French, it will not mean that the person intends to do that. "**Se jeter à l'eau**" means to "**to jump in with both feet**".

For example, you could say the following before doing some paragliding, an extreme sport:

a) J'ai toujours voulu faire du parapente. Bon, cette fois, je vais **me jeter à l'eau** !
À tout à l'heure !
*I have always wanted to go paragliding. Well, this time I am going to **jump in with both feet**! See you later!*

EXERCISES
EXERCICES

The following exercise is more of a game. The list of verbal expressions is (figuratively) endless. It is even common amongst native speakers that they do not know many verbal expressions. The goal of the following exercise is for you to learn some extremely common French verbal expressions that can be used daily while having fun. For this exercise, we do not provide the translations next to the sentences since guessing the meaning of the sentences is also part of the fun. However, we use basic words you probably know very well already. You may use a dictionary too.

1) Listen to the following sentences and try to guess the meaning of the following verbal expressions. Use the context to your advantage.
Devinez la signification des locutions verbales suivantes. Utilisez le contexte à votre avantage.

a) Ce manteau te va comme un gant !

_____.

b) L'homme d'affaires court après l'argent.

_____.

c) Nous tendons la main à tous nos collaborateurs dans ces moments difficiles.

_____.

d) Il a le feu aux trousses !

_____.

e) Mes amis ne mâchent pas leurs mots.

_____.

MOODS

LES MODES

Grammatical modes are **categories of forms** that verbs can take depending on the nuances they are supposed to express. For example, they allow us to conjugate verbs to express something real, something likely, or less likely.

There are two different kinds of modes: **personal modes** and **impersonal modes**.

PERSONAL MOODS
LES MODES PERSONNELS

There are four personal modes: the indicatif (indicative), the subjonctif (subjunctive), the conditionnel (conditional), and the impératif (imperative).

You may have already guessed why those modes are called **personal**. Do you remember *personal verbs?* **Great**. In this case, it refers to almost the same thing. Personal modes are modes in which the verbs can be conjugated with different persons and **not only** the third person singular. Therefore, they have variable conjugated forms. Personal modes allow us to conjugate verbs with different persons.

As we mentioned in the introduction, modes refer to different ways of conjugating verbs depending on the nuance one wishes to add to the sentence: something real, likely, or less likely.

What does this mean concretely? When talking about modes, we are not explicitly talking about how to conjugate verbs. Instead, we are talking about the **values** they have and what **nuances** they add to the sentence.

INDICATIVE
L'INDICATIF

The indicative mode consists of **eight verbal tenses**. Four of them are *simple* in the sense that they are *not conjugated with the help of an auxiliary verb*.

NOTE
The indicative mode is one of the most common modes.

Then, there are four compound tenses, meaning they are conjugated with an auxiliary verb.

The four simple tenses are: the **présent** (the present tense), the **imparfait** (the perfect tense), the **futur simple** (the simple future), and the **passé simple** (the simple past).

Since there are also present or perfect tenses in other modes, when clarification is needed, depending on the context, one can precise we are talking about the **indicatif** by saying **"le présent de l'indicatif"**.

So if you are talking about the indicative imperfect, you can call it **"l'imparfait de l'indicatif"** in French. The same rule applies to **all** tenses. In the following section, you will learn about the subjunctive. For the present tense of the subjunctive mode, you could say **"le présent du subjonctif"**.

The compound tenses of the indicative mode are: the **passé composé** *(compound past)*, the **plus-que-parfait** *(the pluperfect)*, the **futur antérieur** *(the future perfect)*, and the **passé antérieur** *(the past anterior)*. As mentioned in the previous paragraph, you may refer to those tenses followed by "**de l'indicatif**" to clarify which mode you are talking about, e.g., **le plus-que-parfait de l'indicatif**.

1) Values of the present tense
Les valeurs du présent

The present tense is important. You should *know* and *understand* this entire section **well**.

The present tense expresses an action that is **currently happening**. It is the tense we use to *describe and narrate things that are happening right now*.

For example:

a) Je **mange** des cacahuètes.
*I **eat** peanuts.*

b) Jacqueline **part** en vacances.
*Jacqueline **goes** on vacation.*

c) Marie **lit** un livre.
*Mary **reads** a book.*

d) Elles **font** de la randonnée.
*They (fem.) **hike**.*

e) Vous **cuisinez**.
*You (pl.) **cook**.*

It is a tense you will commonly see in novels, as using the present tense makes the *reader feel closer to the story* and its protagonists. **For example:**

In French:

« Je **regarde** ce monstre avec terreur tandis que de la fumée **sort** de ses narines. Vais-je survivre ? Je **mets** une main sur le manche de mon poignard et me **prépare** à combattre. Toutefois, je ne **vois** pas grand-chose dans cette grotte.

In English:

"I **look** at the monster with fear as smoke **comes** out of its nostrils. Will I survive? I **put** a hand on the handle of my dagger and **get** ready to fight. However, I **can** barely see anything in this cave."

In the previous example, all verbs in the present tense are underlined. The only verb not underlined in the present tense is **survivre**: **vais-je survivre**? As you can see, we used the verb **venir + infinitive** as a semi-auxiliary verb to indicate that the protagonist may die **soon** and describe a future that is close to us.

The present tense can also be used in *fixed expressions and sayings* to **express a general truth**.

For example:

a) Le chien **aboie**, la caravane **passe**.
*The dog **barks**, but the caravan **goes on*** (meaning, Let people say what they will).

b) L'habit ne **fait** pas le moine.
***Don't** judge a book by its cover.*

c) Qui se **ressemble**, **s'assemble**.
*Birds of a feather **flock** together.*

The present tense can also be used to express things that are going to happen in the **near future**.

For example:

a) Marie-Louise **va** à Lyon **dans quelques jours**.
*Marie-Louise **is going** to Lyon in a **few days**.*

b) Frédéric **mange** du poisson **ce soir**.
*Frédéric **is going** to eat fish **tonight**.*

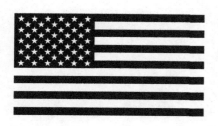

c) Nous **partons** pour les États-Unis **dans un mois**.
*We **are going** to the United States **in one month**.*

Finally, the present tense is also used to express facts or actions that are *regularly repeated in time*.

For example:

a) Je **nage** une fois par jour.
*I **swim** once a day.*

b) Dominique **fait** du cheval deux fois par mois.
*Dominique **goes** horse riding twice a month.*

c) La famille **mange** du gâteau tous les dimanches.
*The family **eats** cake every Sunday.*

2) Values of the simple future
Les valeurs du futur simple

The simple future tense is used to express actions that are going to happen in the future.

For example:

a) J'**irai** au Québec cette année.
*I **will go** to Quebec this year.*

b) Camille **écrira** son mémoire dans deux ans.
*Camille **will write** her dissertation in two years.*

The simple future tense can also be used to express a *posterior action in a narration*.

For example:

a) Marcel obtient son premier poste d'ingénieur en 1988. Il le **quittera** trois ans plus tard.
*Marcel started his first position as an engineer in 1988. He **will quit** three years later.*

Some people use it almost idiomatically in certain contexts to add an additional layer of politeness to the sentence. For example, you will commonly hear the following in shops:

Cela **fera** 9,99€ s'il-vous-plaît.
*It **will be** €9.99, please.*

3) Values of the simple past tense
Les valeurs du passé simple

This is the first time you hear about the simple past in this book. The simple past is (almost) **never** used in oral communication, and when it is, it is in the **formal register**.

In daily life, most people use the compound past instead of the simple past. However, if you are learning French because you are passionate about **literature** written in French, knowing why they use it and recognizing its different forms will probably help you.

The simple past is used to talk about a **unique action**:

a) Nous nous disputâmes. Ensuite, une bouteille de lait tomba. Benoit lâcha immédiatement son livre.
We argued. Then a bottle of milk fell. Benoit immediately dropped his book.

In the above example, you can see that the verbs all refer to unique finished actions.

It is also a succession; the simple past can be used to describe a *succession of events*:

a) Il mangea une pomme, bu une gorgée de café et recommença à dessiner.
He ate an apple, had a sip of coffee, and started drawing again.

It is also used to talk about things that have a *precise beginning and a precise ending*, for example:

a) Notre carrière dura de 1974 à 2004.
Our career lasted from 1974 to 2004.

4) Values of the imperfect
Les valeurs de l'imparfait

The imperfect is used to express things that lasted in time.

For example:

a) Il **mangeait** des carottes tous les jours quand il **était** jeune.
He ate carrots every day when he was young.

b) Les deux frères **conduisaient** tous les week-ends.
The two brothers drove every weekend.

c) Il **avait** des cheveux noirs et blancs. Il **vieillissait** et il s'en **rendait** compte.
His hair was black and white. He was getting old, and he knew it.

The imperfect is also used to describe things, landscapes, or people in the past:

a) La voiture **était** rouge. Le conducteur **était** grand et fort. Son pantalon **avait** des rayures, comme sa voiture.
The car was red. The driver was tall and strong. His pants had stripes, just like his car.

b) La montagne se **tenait** devant nous majestueusement. Son sommet **atteignait** presque les nuages.
The mountain stood in front of us majestically. Its summit almost reached the clouds.

Now, we are going to talk about **compound tenses**. You already know one of them: the **passé composé** or *compound past* or the *perfect tense*. The three others are the **plus-que-parfait** or *pluperfect*, the **passé antérieur** or *past anterior*, and the **futur antérieur** or *future perfect*.

5) Values of the passé composé
Les valeurs du passé composé

The **passé composé** with which you are already familiar is used to refer to an action that is completely finished. This is how you learned how to use it in previous sections.

For example:

a) J'ai mangé une blanquette de veau hier soir.
I ate veal stew yesterday evening.

You ate stew yesterday evening, and the action is completely finished. It is also the tense used alongside the present tense in narrations to refer to an action that happened **before** the action described using the present tense. For example:

a) Je montre à mon cousin ce que j'ai dessiné.
   I am showing my cousin (m.) what I drew.

Your drawing is completely finished, and you are now showing it to your cousin. This is the past tense you can use almost all the time in daily life when you want to describe past actions.

For example:

a) Jean-Louis: Qu'est-ce que tu **as fait** hier soir ?
   What did you do yesterday evening?

b) Patrick: J'**ai joué** à des jeux vidéo, j'**ai nourri** mon chat et j'**ai pris** un bain chaud.
   I played video games, I fed my cat and I had a hot bath.

6) Values of the pluperfect and the past anterior
   Les valeurs du plus-que-parfait et du passé antérieur

The pluperfect and the past anterior are used to refer to actions that happened before an action expressed in the simple past or the imperfect. You do not need to know those tenses perfectly at this point in your learning journey, as they are relatively complex tenses. As mentioned previously, for other tenses, those tenses will be helpful if and when you start reading French literature.

a) Quand elle **fut arrivée** chez sa mère, elles **parlèrent** de son nouveau travail.
   When she arrived at her mother's, they talked about her new job.

"**Quand elle fut arrivée**" is the past anterior form of the verb **arriver**. **Parlèrent** is the simple past form of **parler**. So, the past anterior is used in conjunction with the simple past.

Here is an example of the pluperfect and the imperfect:

a) Marc-Antoine s'**était rendu** à Toulouse pour les vacances, il en **profitait** pour manger les fameuses saucisses de Toulouse.
   Marc-Antoine had been to Toulouse for the holidays, he took advantage of his trip to eat the famous sausages from Toulouse.

S'était rendu is in the pluperfect while **profitait** is in the imperfect. Therefore, the pluperfect is used in conjunction with the imperfect. The act of using the right combination of tenses is called **concordance des temps** in French, *tense concordance* in English.

7) Values of the futur anterior
Les valeurs du futur antérieur

The future anterior tense can be used to refer to the **posteriority** of an action in comparison to another. For example:

> **a)** Je ferai mes devoirs dès que j'**aurai acheté** un nouveau stylo.
> *I will do my homework as soon as I have a new pen.*

In this example, **j'aurai acheté un nouveau stylo** is something that will happen before **"ferai mes devoirs"**. I will have bought a new pen, and **only then** I will do my homework. This is what posteriority means in this context. Having bought a new pen is a posterior action to doing homework.

 It is a very common tense in daily life. Remember how to use this tense well. Later in this book, you will learn how to conjugate verbs in the future anterior tense. You can listen to this example of a daily life conversation:

> **a) Frédéric**: Quand est-ce que tu viens me rendre visite ?
> *When will you come and pay me a visit?*

> **b) Robert**: Je viendrai te rendre visite quand **j'aurai acheté** une nouvelle voiture.
> *I will come visit you when I have a new car.*

> **c) Frédéric**: Super ! Et quand est-ce que tu vas acheter une nouvelle voiture ?
> *Awesome! And when will you buy a new car?*

> **d) Robert**: J'achèterai une nouvelle voiture dès que **j'aurai eu** les sous.
> *I will buy a new car as soon as I have the money.*

The future anterior can also be used on its own to refer to something that will end in the future.

For example:

Nous **aurons terminé** de construire notre maison en 2024.
We will be done building our house in 2024.

In this example, **aurons terminé** is the future anterior. We will come back to this later, but as you can see, conjugating verbs in the future anterior is not difficult: auxiliary verb in the *simple future tense + past participle*. Yes, it is almost like playing Lego! Conjugation is fun!

The future anterior tense can also be used to guess something. Try and remember how to recognize that usage. You do not need to know how to build it, but it is used more relatively often in some parts of the French-speaking world.

For example:

  a) Anna n'est toujours pas là. Sa voiture **sera** sûrement **tombée** en panne.
  Anna is not here yet. Her car probably broke down.

  b) Le réfrigérateur est vide. Mon fils **aura** sûrement tout **mangé**.
  The fridge is empty. My son probably ate everything.

Finally, the future anterior can also be used to talk about something that happened. It is also a subtle usage. You do not need to learn it by heart either but try to recognize it when you hear or see it. For example:

a) Les vacances **auront été** géniales.
  *Literal translation: The holidays **will have been** great.*
  Better translation: The holidays were awesome.

b) Mes amis et moi **auront** bien **rigolé.**
  *Literal translation: My friends and I **will have laughed** a lot.*
  Better translation: My friends and I laughed a lot.

SUBJUNCTIVE
LE SUBJONCTIF

The **subjonctif**, or *subjunctive mode*, consists in four forms: the **présent** (*present tense*) and the **imparfait** (*imperfect*), which are simple tenses (no auxiliary verb in the construction), and the **passé** (*past*) and the **plus-que-parfait** (*pluperfect*).

The subjunctive mode is used to express something uncertain or something without any real temporal precision. Remember that the indicative mode, which you just learned about in the previous section, is used to express something likely, real, or which has a real temporal precision.

Therefore, the subjunctive mode is used with verbs that express a **wish**, a **desire**, an **emotion**, an **obligation**, a **doubt,** or **uncertainty**.

For example:

> **a)** J'aimerais que tu **sois** là.
>   *I wish you were here.*

> **b)** Il faut que tu **ailles** à l'école.
>   *You have to go to school.*

Have you noticed anything particular in these two examples? The word **que** is in both of them, and the subjunctive is what follows the **que**. **Que** means *that*. For now, you can remember that when you see or use the word **que**, if a verb follows it, it is usually conjugated using the subjunctive mode.

While the subjunctive mode can be used on its own, it is mostly used in *subordinate clauses*. A subordinate clause is a part of a sentence that cannot stand alone as a complete sentence. It is connected to the main clause of a sentence using a subordinating conjunction, for example, **que**, as we saw in the previous paragraph.

1) Values of the present tense in the subjunctive mode
Les valeurs du présent du subjonctif

The present tense of the subjunctive mode is used to refer to an *uncertain action*, not carried out at the moment when the sentence is being said.

For example:

> **a)** Elle souhaite que ses amis lui **disent** la vérité.
> *She wishes her friends would tell her the truth.*

In this example, the action is **not finished** and has not even started. We are not sure whether her friends tell her the truth or not either. Note that the verb **disent** is the verb dire in the present tense of the subjunctive mode.

More examples:

> **a)** Mon père ne pense pas que je **puisse** réparer la voiture.
> *My father does not think that I can fix the car.*

> **b)** Il faut que nous **partions,** car il est tard.
> *We have to go because it is late.*

As mentioned before, you can notice **que** in both sentences. In the first sentence, you can see that in the English translation. The verb **pouvoir** *(can)* is in the subjunctive form: **puisse**. You will learn more about the different forms later. In the second sentence, there is no that in the English translation because we are using the idiomatic expression **il faut que** (infinitive form: **falloir que**) which you have seen in the section about impersonal verbs.

2) Values of the past tense in the subjunctive mode
Les valeurs du passé du subjonctif

The past tense of the subjunctive mode is used to describe an **uncertain** action but which we suppose is **finished** at the time of speaking.

For example:

> **a)** Je ne crois pas qu'il **ait fini** les restes.
> *I do not think that he finished the leftovers.*

As mentioned before, you can see the **que** *(that)* in the sentence followed by the verb **finir** *(to finish)* in the past tense of the subjunctive mot. The action **finir les restes** *(to finish the leftovers)* is finished, but we are not certain it happened.

Another example:

> **a)** Je ne pense pas que mes parents **aient acheté** un ordinateur.
> *I do not think that my parents bought a computer.*

You can see the verb **acheter** in the past tense of the subjunctive mode in this example. The action, once again, is finished, but we are not sure the parents actually bought the computer.

3) Values of the imperfect in the subjunctive mode
Les valeurs de l'imparfait du subjonctif

The imperfect tense of the subjunctive mode is **mainly used in literature. You will almost never hear it in daily oral communication except maybe in a humoristic context**. When speakers of English make jokes about ancient times or royalty, they use expressions such as *thou art*, using the imperfect tense of the subjunctive in oral communication is sometimes done as a joke amongst speakers of French to pretend they are members of a royal family or that they are from the past.

You do not need to learn it at this stage, yet it is interesting to know it exists. As usual, you may encounter it in literature, and knowing how to recognize what verb it is could be helpful. The imperfect tense of the subjunctive mode is a simple tense (no auxiliary), which is used to describe an uncertain and unfinished action at the moment when the speaker was talking. For example:

> **a)** Je ne pensais pas que ce plat **fût** aussi mauvais.
> *I did not think that that dish was that bad.*

Once again, you can see the **que** (*that*) followed by the verb **être** (*to be*) in the imperfect tense of the subjunctive.

4) Values of the pluperfect in the subjunctive mode
Les valeurs du plus-que-parfait du subjonctif

Finally, the pluperfect of the subjunctive mode **is also mostly used in literature**. It is used to describe an **uncertain** but **supposedly finished** action at the moment when the speaker was talking.

> **a)** Je ne pensais pas qu'il **eût rendu** la voiture à ses parents.
> *I did not think that he had given the car back to his parents.*

As usual, you can see the **que** *(that)* in the sentence followed by **rendre** *(to give back)* in the pluperfect tense of the subjunctive.

When you reach a B1+ - B2 (upper intermediate) level in French, learning and understanding those forms will help you reach a C1 (advanced) level. For now, you need to understand when to use the **present and past** tenses of the subjunctive. You will learn how to conjugate them properly in the next sections. **Remember their respective values and usages**.

CONDITIONAL
LE CONDITIONNEL

The conditional mode consists of a **present tense** and a **past tense**.

The present tense of the conditional is formed using the radical of the verb in the future tense of the indicative followed by the ending of the imperfect of the indicative.

For example:

Let us consider the verb **couper** *(to cut)*. Its radical in the future tense is **couper**, as you have seen in the first sections of this book.

Therefore:

COUPER	TO CUT
Radical : **couper**	Root: **couper**
je couper**ais**	I would cut
tu couper**ais**	you would cut
il / elle / on couper**ait**	he/she/it would cut
nous couper**ions**	we would cut
vous couper**iez**	you would cut
ils / elles couper**aient**	they would cut

Do you recognize the endings of the imperfect here?

There are two forms of the past tense in the conditional mode. Only the first one is important for you, as the second one is barely used at all except in (mostly classic) literature.

The first form of the past of the conditional mode is formed using an auxiliary verb followed by the past participle. Let us see what it means for the verb **couper:**

j'aur**ais** coupé	I will have cut
tu aur**ais** coupé	you will have cut
il / elle / on aur**ait** coupé	he/she/it will have cut
nous aur**ions** coupé	we will have cut
vous aur**iez** coupé	you will have cut
ils / elles aur**aient** coupé	they will have cut

1) Values of the conditional mode
Les valeurs du mode conditionnel

The conditional mode is used to describe unreal facts or actions which are possible, but **which require a condition to be fulfilled**. For example:

a) **Conditional present**: Si j'avais un animal de compagnie, je lui **achèterais** plein de jouets.
If I had a pet, I would buy it a lot of toys.

b) **Conditional past:** Si j'étais riche, **j'aurais acheté** plusieurs instruments de musique à mes enfants.
If I were rich, I would have bought several musical instruments for my children.

You probably noticed a pattern in these two examples. The first part of the sentence is constructed with **si + a verb in the imperfect**, and the following part of the sentence is built as explained above. In both cases, we express a condition necessary to carry out the second part of the sentence. Both sentences describe unrealistic situations.

The conditional can also be used to express a **supposition** or something **uncertain**:

> **a)** Avec toutes ses compétences, elle **devrait** être milliardaire.
> *With all her skills, she should be a billionaire.*

It is not reality; it is a supposition.

Another example:

> **a)** Je pense que ce joueur de badminton **gagnerait** à être connu.
> *I think this badminton player deserves to be known.*

Once again, it is not a reality but a supposition.

The conditional can also be used to express something **unreal** or a **fictional desire**.

> **a)** Je rêve de devenir diplomate. Je **voyagerais** dans beaucoup de pays et je **rencontrerais** des présidents et des célébrités.
> *I dream of becoming a diplomat. I would travel in many countries and I would meet presidents and famous people.*

In this example, all of this is only a dream but nothing concrete.

The conditional can also be used to add a **layer of politeness**. For example:

> **a) Accepteriez**-vous (sing.) de me prêter ce livre ?
> *Literal translation: would you (sing. form.) accept to lend me this book?*
> *Better and more accurate translation: Would you be so kind as to lend me this book?*

REMINDER

Remember that **vous** can be used as **tu** in formal contexts. You use it when you do not know someone well or in formal contexts, e.g., in shops, in administrative offices, when talking to a teacher, etc. Please also note that people are less likely to use **vous** even when talking to strangers in some French-speaking parts of the world. If you are unsure whether you should use **tu** or **vous**, ask the person about which pronoun they are more comfortable using.

Another example:

a) Pourriez-vous m'aider à porter mes bagages s'il vous plaît ?
Literal translation: Could you please help me carry my luggage?
Better translation: Would you be kind as to help me carry my luggage, please?

The conditional mode can also be used to talk about something **posterior** to something in the past. In French, we describe this usage as **futur dans le passé** or **futur du passé**, which would be future in the past or future of the past. For example:

a) Quand j'étais **petit, je pensais que je deviendrais président.**
When I was little, I thought I would become president.

NOTE

It can sometimes be difficult to differentiate the future of the indicative mode from the conditional.

For example:

a) Je **deviendrai** = I will become

b) Je **deviendrais** = I would become

TIP

To check whether the verb is in the future tense of the indicative or conditional, you can *replace the pronoun*.

For example:

a) Quand je serai grand, je **deviendrai** juge.
When I am an adult, I will become a judge.

You can replace je with il / elle / on in the sentence:

b) Quand il sera grand, il **deviendra** juge.
When he is an adult, he will become a judge.

By replacing the pronoun, you can see the verb is in the future tense.

Second example with the conditional:

a) Quand j'étais petit, je pensais que je **deviendrais** fermier.
When I was little, I thought I would become a farmer.

Now, you can replace the pronoun like before:

b) Quand il était enfant, il pensait qu'il **deviendrait** fermier.
When he was little, he thought he would become a farmer.

Finally, you have to be very careful with the conditional, as native speakers of French often make mistakes when building sentences using the conditional mode. The most famous example in the French language is the sentence:

a) Had I known, I would not have come.

You will often hear:

b) Si **j'aurais** su, je ne **serais** pas venu. - this is **extremely wrong**.

c) Si **j'avais** su, je ne **serais** pas venu. - this is the **correct form**.

The conditional does not follow **si**; it comes in the **second clause** of the sentence.

IMPERATIVE
L'IMPÉRATIF

The **impératif**, or imperative mode in English, is a mode used to express an **order**, a **piece of advice**, a **request** or a **recommendation** to be realized or fulfilled in a **near or distant future**. Its values are similar to that of the imperative in English. For example:

a) Fais-ça !
Do it!

b) Mange tes légumes !
Eat your vegetables!

The imperative mode has two tenses; the **present tense and past tense**. In the imperative mode, **verbs can be conjugated using only three persons: the second person singular, and the first and second person plurals**. Moreover, another critical point to remember is that pronouns are not used when conjugating verbs in the imperative mode, which means **tu**, **nous** and **vous** *will not appear in sentences written in the imperative mode*. For example:

a) Ouvre la porte !
Open the door!

b) Cherchons les clefs !
Let us look for the keys!

c) Aidez (second person plural) moi !
Help me! (you, pl.)

As you can see, no personal pronoun is to be seen in any of those sentences. Also, you may have noticed a pattern already: the conjugated forms of the verb in the imperative mode are really close to the conjugated forms of the verb in the present tense of the indicative mode but without the **s** at the end for the second person singular.

For example:

a) Present of the indicative mode: Tu **fermes** la fenêtre.
You close the window.

b) Present of the imperative mode: Ferme la fenêtre!
Close the window!

As you can see, there is no **s** at the end of **ferme** in the present tense of the imperative mode.

---

1) Notes on the past tense of the imperative mode:

The past tense of the imperative is a compound tense built using the auxiliary verbs **avoir** *(to have)* and **être** *(to be)*. Then, the main verb is conjugated using its past participle, like when you conjugate verbs in the perfect tense or compound past.

The past tense of the imperative mode is rarely used. Its purpose is to express anteriority compared to an action that is not yet realized.

For example:

> **a) Aie** rangé ta chambre avant le dîner !
> *You better have your room tidied before dinner.*

> **b) Sois** parti avant lundi !
> *You better be gone by Monday!*

You may have noticed another oddity here. The forms of **être** and **avoir** in the imperative mode are built using their subjunctive form and not their indicative form. We will come back to this later in this book.

IMPERSONAL MOODS
LES MODES IMPERSONNELS

Then, there are impersonal modes: the **infinitive**, the **participle**, and the **gerundive**.

Again, you know what impersonal verbs are, so you may have also guessed what impersonal modes are. However, in this case, the rule is a bit stricter. Indeed, in impersonal modes, the verbs cannot be conjugated with any person whatsoever.

INFINITIVE
L'INFINITIF

The infinitive, with which you are already familiar since the first sections of this book, is an impersonal mode which which expresses an idea of the action without referring to a person, number, or time. *Knowing whether the action is real or not is impossible with the infinitive form*. The infinitive consists of two tenses: the **present tense,** which is a simple tense (no auxiliary required to build it), and the **past tense,** which is a compound form in the infinitive mode. For example:

First example with avoir:

> **a) Manger**
> *To eat*

> **b) Avoir mangé**
> *To have eaten*

Second example with avoir:

> **a) Nager**
> *To swim*

> **b) Avoir nagé**
> *To have swum*

First example with être:

> **a) Partir**
> *To leave*

> **b) Être parti**
> *To have left*

Second example with être:

a) Se laver
To wash oneself

b) S'être lavé
To have washed oneself

The infinitive mode has only two kinds of values. Its first value is of an entirely **verbal nature**. Its second **value is nominative**. However, the former is the value you will encounter the most in the French language.

1) Verbal values

It can be used with a subject that is different from the main one in what is known as an infinitive proposition. For example:

a) Je vois le chien **passer**.
I see the dog pass by.

When conjugating a verb, it can be used without its own subject in certain cases, such as in infinitive groups that function as indirect object complements or adverbial phrases.

For example:

b) Je me suis dépêché **d'aller** chez le dentiste.
*Literal translation: I hurried **to go** to the dentist.*
Better translation: I hurried and went to the dentist.

c) J'ai acheté des œufs pour **faire** une omelette.
*I bought eggs **to make** an omelette.*

d) Elle cherche une paire de chaussettes pour **aller** dans les montagnes.
*She is looking for a pair of socks **to go** in the mountains.*

In the previous examples, you can see that the infinitive verbs are also used in English sentences. There are many similarities! The infinitive can also be used without its own subject in what we call indirect interrogative subordinate clauses. Wait... Indirect interrogative subordinate clause...? Once again, those are scary words to describe something very simple. It refers to the action of asking a question without it being in an interrogative tone. In simple terms, it is a **question that is asked indirectly**.

For example:

    a) Direct interrogation: "What is your name?" he asked.

    b) Indirect interrogative subordinate clause: He asked what my name was.

Back to the infinitive in indirect interrogative subordinate clauses, let us see an example in French:

    a) Je ne sais pas **quoi** lui **dire**.
    I do not know what to tell her/him.

This sentence could be asked in the form of a direct question: *What should I tell her/him?*

The infinitive can also be found in independent or main clauses. It can then be used to express an **interrogation** or a **doubt**:

    a) Que dire ?
    What is there to say?

    b) Que faire en Islande ?
    What is there to do in Iceland?

The infinitive can also be used to express an **order**, a **piece of advice,** or **instructions,** such as in recipes.

For example:

    a) Mélanger les œufs et la farine.
    Mix the eggs and the flour.

    b) Ajouter du lait.
    Add some milk.

    c) Mélanger à nouveau.
    Mix again.

    d) Laisser reposer.
    Leave the mix to rest.

It can also be used to express an **exclamative** or **interrogative** sentence:

a) Exclamative : Payer un tel prix pour une voiture ! Quelle idée saugrenue!

Paying such a high price for a car! What a strange idea!

b) Interrogative: Comment **savoir** si c'est la bonne taille?

How do I know if it is the right size?

2) Nominal values

The infinitive can also have the value of a **noun**, whether an article precedes it or not. The infinitive form can serve **all the functions of a nominal group**. For example, it can serve the purpose of a **subject**:

a) Dessiner est une passion.

Drawing *is a passion.*

b) Travailler est une necessité.

Working *is a necessity.*

c) Jouer est important pour les enfants.

Playing *is important for children.*

The infinitive can also play the role of the **attribute of a subject**. For example:

a) Ce n'est pas **progresser** ça !

You call that progress ?

b) Tu rigoles ! Ce n'est pas **gagner** ça !

Are you joking ? You call that a win?

Do you remember what direct (COD), indirect (COI), and second object (COS) complements are? **Great, because the infinitive can also play their role**!

a) COD: Ils veulent **s'asseoir** à notre table.

*They want **to sit** at our table.*

b) COI: Il refuse **de partir**.

*He refuses **to leave**.*

c) COS: Nous invitons nos amis **à venir**.

*We invite our friends **to come over**.*

The infinitive can also play the role of **adverbial phrases**. For example:

> **a) Adverbial phrase of time:** L'enfant rangera **avant de jouer**.
> *The child will tidy up before playing.*

The infinitive can also play the role of an **apposition**. In simple terms, an apposition is when two or more words or phrases are grammatically parallel. For example:

> **a)** French President, Jacques Chirac, + rest of the sentence.

Jacques Chirac is the **apposition** in this example because it serves the same function as French President and is used in parallel.

Example with an infinitive serving the role of an apposition:

> **a)** Je n'ai qu'une envie, **voyager**.
> *I have only one wish, **to travel**.*

The infinitive can also be used as a possessive phrase. If you are familiar with grammar cases, this is what corresponds to the genitive. The genitive in grammar refers to possession. In French, to express possession, we often use **de**.

For example:

> **a)** L'ordinateur **de** Thierry.
> *Thierry**'s** computer.*

's is used to form the genitive in English.

The infinitive can be used in such a way too:

> **a)** La joie **de vivre**.
> *The joy of living.*
>
> **b)** La peur **de mourir**.
> *The fear of death.*

As you can see in these two examples, it is as if **joie** and **peur** respectively "belonged" to **vivre** (*to live*) and to **mourir** (*to die*).

Finally, the infinitive can also be used as a **complement of the adjective**. For example:

a) C'est agréable **à entendre**.
It is pleasant to hear.

b) Ce livre est intéressant **à lire**.
It is an interesting book to read.

FINAL NOTE

When you add le before a verb, it becomes a **substantive** (a **noun**). For example:

a) Le rire, c'est bon pour la santé.
Literal translation: The laugh, it is good for the health.
Better translation: Laughing is good for your health.

b) Son but ultime, c'est **le pouvoir**.
His ultimate goal is power.

Note that in the final sentence, **pouvoir** means *can* or *to be able to* in English. In French, power refers to being able to do something.

PARTICIPLE
LE PARTICIPE

The *participle*, also known as the *present participle* or **participe présent** in French, is a verbal form that refers to an action and that can have an object complement or an adverbial phrase. The participle is **invariable**. It is built using the radical of the verb with the first person plural in the present tense of the indicative mode to which we add the ending **-ant**.

Example with the verb aller (to go):

a) How do you find the present participle of aller?

b) First, you conjugate it in the first personal plural (**nous** / we): **Nous allons**.

c) Second, you just keep the root: **all.**

d) Then you add **ant** to it: **allant**.

Second example with the verb marcher (to walk):

    a) How do you find the present participle of **marcher**?

    b) First, you conjugate it in the first personal plural (nous / we): **Nous marchons**.

    c) Second, you just keep the root: **march.**

    d) Then you add **ant** to it: **marchant**.

When the present participle is used in its verbal form followed by an object complement or an adverbial phrase, it remains invariable. For example:

    a) Voilà un livre **intéressant** pour les parents et les enfants.
       Here is a book which is of interest for parents and children.

In this example, **intéressant** is the present participle of the verb **intéresser** *(to interest)*. You recognize it is a present participle form because you can replace it with **qui intéresse**, meaning which interests.

GERUNDIVE
LE GÉRONDIF

The *gerundive* or **gérondif** in French is the adverbial form of the verb. Like an adverb, it *clarifies the meaning of the verb in the sentence*. Be careful, the gerundive is very similar to the present participle, but they are not the same. As we saw, the present participle in the previous section, refers to a noun or pronoun whereas the gerundive modifies a verb. Furthermore, the present participle in its verbal form **tends to refer to a state** whereas the gerundive is used to **put an emphasis** on the action while remaining invariable.

Recognizing the gerundive is easier than recognizing the present participle because the gerundive is preceded by **en**.

    a) En cherchant ses clefs, il aperçu une note sur le mur.
       While looking *for his keys, he noticed a note on his wall.*

    b) En courant, il écoute de la musique.
       While running, *he listens to music.*

In these two examples, you can see that the gerundive refers to simultaneous actions, but that is not its only purpose. It can also be used to express a manner or way of doing something.

Examples of both:

a) Simultaneity: Il ne téléphone pas **en conduisant**.
He does not use his phone while driving.

b) Way of doing something: C'est **en pratiquant** qu'on apprend le mieux.
Learning by doing is the best.

Additional information on the gerundive:

The word **tout** (*all*) can be added in front of the gerundive to express simultaneity as well:

a) Tout en respectant ta décision, je ne l'approuve pas.
All while respecting your decision, I do not approve of it.

EXERCISES
EXERCICES

1) Identify the mode and tense of the verbs in bold.

Identifiez le mode et le temps des verbes en gras.

a) Claudine **aimerait** aller au restaurant avec Pascale plus souvent.

Claudine would like to go to the restaurant with Pascale more often.

_____.

b) Les étudiants **ayant fini** leur examen peuvent sortir de la salle.

Students who are done with their exam can leave the room.

_____.

c) La maison n'est pas finie ! Il **aurait fallu** commencer plus tôt.

The house is not finished yet! We should have started building it earlier.

_____.

d) Il est possible que nous ne **soyons pas rentrés** avant la tombée de la nuit à ce rythme.

We may not be home before nightfall at this pace.

_____.

e) Préparons à manger tous les dimanches pour être tranquille pendant la semaine.

Let us prepare food every Sunday for the rest of the week so that we do not have to do it during the week when we are tired.

_____.

f) Lorsque vous **étiez** en Argentine, on jouait avec votre chien tous les jours.

When you were in Argentina, we played with your dog every day.

_____.

g) Carine aurait souhaité que vous **trouvassiez** la réponse par vous-même (pl.).

Carine wished you had found the answer by yourselves.

_____.

h) Je bois du thé **en jouant** aux mots croisés.

I drink tea while playing crosswords.

---

i) Quand Jean-Marc **fut arrivé** au travail, il crut qu'il avait oublié ses clefs sur la porte de sa maison.

When Jean-Marc arrived at work, he thought he had forgotten his keys on the door of his house.

---

j) Si j'avais commencé à apprendre à jouer de la flûte plus jeune, **j'aurais** un bien meilleur niveau maintenant.

If I had started learning how to play the flute when I was younger, I would have a much better level now.

---

k) Ayant moyennement faim, nous préférons manger une soupe aujourd'hui.

We prefer having a soup today since we are not that hungry.

---

l) Est-ce que tu pourras m'aider quand tu **auras fini** de regarder la télévision?

Help me when you are done watching television, will you?

---

m) Il se peut que vous **arriviez** plus tard parce que les avions sont souvent en retard en ce moment.

You are likely going to arrive late because planes are often delayed these days.

---

n) Finissons vite nos devoirs pour aller jouer dehors après !

Let us quickly finish our homework to go and play outside after.

---

o) Ayez fini cette tâche avant ce soir. Ensuite, vous **pourrez** nous rejoindre pour le barbecue.

Finish this task by tonight. Then, you will be able to join us at the barbecue.

REGULAR AND IRREGULAR VERBS

LES VERBES RÉGULIERS ET IRRÉGULIERS

In this section, you will mostly learn about irregular verbs in more detail.

REGULAR
RÉGULIER

You have already learned about regular verbs in the first part of this book. They are verbs that belong to the first and second groups. The infinitive form of verbs belonging to the first group end in -**er**. The infinitive form of regular verbs belonging to the second group end in **-ir**, and their present participle form end in -**issant**. If you struggle to recognize verbs of the first and second groups, do not hesitate and go back to previous sections. Do not forget that you are allowed to use a dictionary or a Bescherelle to check the present participle form of verbs ending in **ir** in their infinitive form.

Regular verbs are verbs for which all the conjugated forms are regular, which means the endings of these two kinds of verbs are always the same even if there are a few oddities, especially when it comes to slight changes in the radical of some verbs.

IRREGULAR
IRRÉGULIER

Now, let us focus on irregular verbs and jump in with both feet. Just like in English, there are irregular verbs in French. Irregular verbs in French are slightly more complex than in English, though. In English, irregularity is mostly expressed through the forms a verb can have in the past tenses: swim, swam, swum.

As you may remember (**congratulations** if you do!) from the first section of this book, irregular verbs are *verbs belonging to the third group*. Defective verbs are also considered irregular verbs. Defective verbs are verbs that cannot be conjugated in all possible forms. We will come back to this later in this section.

Why do irregular verbs exist in French? Not to annoy you, that is for sure! To put it simply, some verbs are irregular because they have been in use for a very long time in the French language, and over time, their radical has changed. Some of these verbs have also gone through a fusion of their different radicals throughout history. You may find it reassuring to know that when new verbs are introduced in the French language, they are always regular. Irregular verbs are not added to the language anymore.

You know that a regular verb is a verb whose different conjugated forms always follow the same patterns. On the other hand, irregular verbs are verbs whose conjugated forms are unique. Some verbs are considered completely irregular: **aller** *(to go)*, **dire** *(to say)*, **faire** *(to do / to make)*, **pouvoir** *(can / to be able to)*, **savoir** (to know), **valoir** *(to be worth)*, **vouloir** *(to want)*. You already know a lot of those verbs:

The verbs **aller**, **dire**, **faire**, **savoir** and **vouloir** have been used extensively throughout this book. You probably know how to conjugate them in some common tenses already thanks to exposure.

The verbs **pouvoir** and **valoir** were introduced in the section about impersonal verbs. Thanks to exposure, you probably also know how to conjugate them in the most commonly used tenses.

Verbs that belong to the third group and end with **ir** or **ïr** are those whose present participle does not end with **issant**.

Finally, the other kind of verbs belonging to the third group consists of verbs whose infinitive form ends with **-re** or **-oir**. Those verbs are less common than those ending in **-ir**.

For example: **asseoir** *(to sit)*, **avoir** *(to have)*, **devoir** *(to owe / must / to have to)*, **émouvoir** *(to move / to stir / to affect / to touch)*, **falloir** *(to need / to have to do)*, **pleuvoir** *(to rain)*, **pouvoir** *(to be able to / can)*, **recevoir** *(to receive)*, savoir *(to know)*, **valoir** *(to be worth)*, **vouloir** *(to want)*, and **voir** *(to see)*.

Impersonal verbs, with which you are familiar already, are defective verbs. They are commonly used to describe the weather: **pleuvoir** *(to rain)*, **neiger** *(to snow)*, etc. There are other verbs in the defective verbs category but almost all are barely used except in (classic) literature. Most native speakers of French do not even know them. Let us have some fun with an example, though. The verb **chaloir** is a defective verb that does not exist in any other form but the infinitive and in one idiomatic expression:

a) Peu me chaut.
I do not care.

b) Peu lui chaut.
He/she/it does not care.

This sentence belongs to the formal register and can be seen almost only in classic literature these days. This is also the only use case of the verb **chaloir**. It cannot be used in any other way or sentence.

Now, we have seen that irregular verbs end with **ir**, **ïr**, **re**, and **oir** are irregular verbs. These are the general endings. They can be declined into more specific endings. An exhaustive list of all endings is:

a) oir, oire, dre, ir, oudre, oindre, tre, aindre, and eindre.

As you can see, saying they end with **ir**, **ïr**, **re** and **oir** is not wrong. All the other endings are just variations. Now, we are going to see some examples, and examples only. Indeed, there are *over three hundred irregular verbs* in French, so you have to learn them individually as you progress in your learning journey, just like in English or German. A relatively exhaustive list of irregular verbs and their translation can be found at the end of this book.

At least, there is one easy thing that you can apply even with irregular verbs: when you know their past participle, you can always conjugate them in the perfect tense (reminder: also known as compound past) without too many variations. For example, the past participle of **boire** is **bu**, so if you want to conjugate it in the perfect tense:

BOIRE	TO DRINK
Participe passé : **bu**	Past participle: **bu**
j'ai **bu**	I drank
tu as **bu**	you drank
il/elle/on a **bu**	he/she/it drank
nous avons **bu**	we drank
vous avez **bu**	you drank
ils/elles ont **bu**	they drank

Simple tenses (those without an auxiliary) are more challenging. So let us see a few examples in the present tense of the indicative mode. There will be quite a few tables in the following subsections, but you do not need to learn them by heart. Instead, try and remember how to recognize those verbs and their endings in the present tense. When you start recognizing patterns, you will be able to use them in your daily life, maybe with mistakes at first, but practice makes perfect. Also, remember that when learning a language, to remain motivated, it is always good to learn the words and structures you use very often to start practicing as soon as possible.

To make the best use possible of the next section, try and guess the endings of the verbs in the present tense of the indicative mode instead of just skimming and scanning the tables.

In section 10.2.10, there will be a recap with general rules for the most common verbs, which should help you conjugate any irregular verb in the present tense of the indicative.

VERBS WHICH END WITH OIRE

BOIRE	TO DRINK
je b**ois**	I drink
tu b**ois**	you drink
il/elle/on b**oit**	he/she/it drinks
nous b**uvons**	you drink
vous b**uvez**	we drink
ils/elles b**oivent**	they drink

VERBS WHICH END WITH OIR

First example:

SAVOIR	TO KNOW
je s**ais**	I know
tu s**ais**	you know
il/elle/on s**ait**	he/she/it knows
nous s**avons**	we know
vous s**avez**	you know
ils/elles s**avent**	they know

Second example:

PRÉVOIR	TO PREDICT
je prév**ois**	I predict
tu prév**ois**	you predict
il/elle/on prév**oit**	he/she/it predicts
nous prév**oyons**	we predict
vous prév**oyez**	you predict
ils/elles prév**oient**	they predict

Note that in this case, if you remove **pré** from **prévoir**, you get the verb **voir** (*to see*), and the conjugation follows the same pattern, so you just have to remove **pré** from the conjugated forms to conjugate **voir**.

VERBS WHICH END WITH AINDRE OR EINDRE

The endings are the same for both kinds. Let us see two examples.

First example:

PLAINDRE	TO PITY
je pl**ains**	I pity
tu pl**ains**	you pity
il/elle/ont pl**aint**	he/she/it pities
nous pl**aignons**	we pity
vous pl**aignez**	you pity
ils/elles pl**aignent**	they pity

Second example:

PEINDRE	TO PAINT
je p**eins**	I paint
tu p**eins**	you paint
il/elle/on p**eint**	he/she/it paints
nous p**eignons**	we paint
vous p**eignez**	you paint
ils/elles p**eignent**	they paint

As you can see, the endings for both examples are the same.

VERBS WHICH END WITH DRE

MORDRE	TO BITE
je m**ors**	I bite
tu m**ors**	you bite
il/elle/on m**ord**	he/she/it bites
nous m**ordons**	we bite
vous m**ordez**	you bite
ils/elles m**ordent**	they bite

VERBS WHICH END WITH IR

DORMIR	TO SLEEP
je d**ors**	I sleep
tu d**ors**	you sleep
il/elle/on d**ort**	he/she/it sleeps
nous d**ormons**	we sleep
vous d**ormez**	you sleep
ils/elles d**orment**	they sleep

VERBS WHICH END WITH OUDRE

First example:

COUDRE	TO SEW
je c**ouds**	I sew
tu c**ouds**	you sew
il/elle/on c**oud**	he/she/it sews
nous c**ousons**	we sew
vous c**ousez**	you sew
ils/elles c**ousent**	they sew

Second example:

MOUDRE	TO MILL
je m**ouds**	I mill
tu m**ouds**	you mill
il/elle/on m**oud**	he/she/it mills
nous m**oulons**	we mill
vous m**oulez**	you mill
ils/elles m**oulent**	they mill

VERBS WHICH END WITH OINDRE

There are only a dozen verbs that end with **oindre** and most of them are barely used. The most important one is **joindre**.

JOINDRE	TO JOIN
je j**oins**	I join
tu j**oins**	you join
il/elle/on j**oint**	he/she/it joins
nous j**oignons**	we join
vous j**oignez**	you join
ils/elles j**oignent**	they join

VERBS WHICH END WITH TRE

METTRE	TO PUT
je m**ets**	I put
tu m**ets**	you put
il/elle/on m**et**	he/she/it puts
nous m**ettons**	we put
vous m**ettez**	you put
ils/elles m**ettent**	they put

VERBS WHICH END WITH IR

Some verbs ending in **ir** have the same endings as verbs that belong to the first group. These verbs are: **cueillir** *(to pick / to pluck)*, **offrir** *(to offer)*, **ouvrir** *(to open)*, **souffrir** *(to suffer)*. Let us consider two examples.

First example:

OFFRIR	TO OFFER
j'offr**e**	I offer
tu offr**es**	you offer
il/elle/on offr**e**	he/she/it offers
nous offr**ons**	we offer
vous offr**ez**	you offer
ils/elles offr**ent**	they offer

Second example:

OUVRIR	TO OPEN
j'ouvr**e**	I open
tu ouvr**es**	you open
il/elle/on ouvr**e**	he/she/it opens
nous ouvr**ons**	we open
vous ouvr**ez**	you open
ils/elles ouvr**ent**	they open

RECAP

a) Most verbs of the third group have the following endings: **s, s, t, ons, ez, ent**

b) Verbs which end with **dre** like **vendre** *(to sell)*, **perdre** *(to lose)* or **coudre** *(to sew)* end with: **ds, ds, d, ons, ez, ent.**

c) Except those which end with **aindre**, **eindre**, **oindre** like **craindre**, **peindre**, **joindre**, **résoudre** which follow the general rule: **s, s, t, ons, ez, ent**.

d) The verbs **pouvoir**, **vouloir**, and **valoir** with which you are very familiar by now end with: **x, x, t, ons, ez, ent**.

e) And finally, many of the verbs ending in **ir** and belonging to the third group have the same endings as regular verbs of the first group: **e, es, e, ons, ez, ent**.

EXERCISES
EXERCICES

1) Listen to the following sentences and insert the missing verbs.
Écoutez les phrases suivantes et insérez les verbes manquants.

The translation is provided in the Answer Key. Focus on the sounds. Listen to the sentences again if you are not sure about a verb. If the text is extremely easy for you; it means your current level in French should be about B1- (lower intermediate). If the text is relatively easy for you; it means your current level is A – A+ (upper beginner). If you struggle with the text at this point, do not hesitate to go back to previous sections and review the content that was difficult for you. If the vocabulary is too complicated, do not hesitate and go back to the French Made Easy Level 1 and the French Picture Dictionary books by Lingo Mastery. Now, good luck. This is one of the most important exercises in this book!

Ce matin, mes enfants, Dominique et Henri, _____ à l'école à bicyclette.

À l'école, ils _____ souvent des activités ludiques comme de la peinture,

du sport, de la sculpture, et même des gâteaux en cours de cuisine. Ce que Dominique

_____, c'est _____ au badminton en cours de sport.

Henri, lui, _____ les cours d'arts plastiques. Il _____ déjà

énormément en temps normal à la maison.

La semaine prochaine, tous les élèves de leur classe _____ en Angleterre

en voyage de classe. La maîtresse d'école _____ à deux parents d'élèves

de _____ avec eux. J'ai proposé de _____ et cela

_____, donc c'est sûr, j'y _____ !

Apparemment, il _____ souvent en Angleterre, on _____

bien le temps une fois sur place. Puis, nous _____ à travers

tout le pays donc le temps ne _____ sûrement pas le même partout.

Quand les élèves _____ en cours, ils seront sûrement tristes d'avoir

quitté l'Angleterre. Ils _____ tous hâte d'y _____.

Le seul problème _____ que les enfants _____

dans des familles chez leurs correspondants. Pour nous, les deux parents d'élèves

accompagnateurs, rien _____ encore _____. Cependant,

je _____ sûre que ce problème _____ rapidement.

TENSES
LES TEMPS

In the previous sections, you have learned a lot of things: the basics, how French verbs are classified, and what regular and irregular verbs are. You have also learned the basics about French conjugation using the most used tenses.

When conjugating verbs, you should know how to choose the correct person, singular or plural (je, tu il/elle/on, nous, vous, ils/elles) as well as the correct tense to use. That is the first step to conjugate verbs properly. When talking about tenses, we also have to talk about time. Tenses intrinsically relate to time. When did the state or action take place?

Generally speaking, we can think of time as a concept divided into three categories: past, present, and future. However, there are over twenty tenses in French. How is that possible? As we have seen in the previous sections, French grammar also uses moods (les modes) to indicate how speakers feel about the state or action. Do not worry, though: many of them are not commonly used. Some of them are also primarily used in writing but not when speaking.

In this unit, you will study the most important tenses in-depth, including by practising with exercises. The least common tenses will be mentioned, and you will understand how to recognize them in context and why they are used. Of course, we will mention it when you do not need to learn those specific tenses by heart. However, there are also tenses you will need to understand in-depth, and they will be mentioned.

Finally, this is the last section of the book. Its purpose is to practice everything you have learned so far and to deepen your knowledge of the foundations so that you can continue building on solid basics. Therefore, we will focus on exercises, and those exercises will allow you to apply everything you know. The exercises will aim to test your listening and reading comprehension, writing ability, and grammar and vocabulary.

INDICATIVE
L'INDICATIF

PRESENT
LE PRÉSENT

Le passé c'est de l'ancien présent.

C'est fou non?

Et dans le futur, le présent ça sera du passé.

L'avenir du présent c'est le futur.

We will not cover the present tense of the indicative mode again in this section because you should be very comfortable with it by now. Here is a reminder of the endings for verbs belonging to the first and second groups.

FIRST GROUP	
je	-e
tu	-es
il/elle/on	-e
nous	-ons
vous	-ez
ils/elles	-ent

SECOND GROUP	
je	-s
tu	-s
il/elle/on	-t
nous	-sson
vous	-ssez
ils/elles	-ssent

EXERCISES
EXERCICES

1) You will hear five sentences in French. After each sentence, you will have a few seconds to guess the infinitive form of the verb used in the sentence.

Vous allez entendre cinq phrases en français. Après chaque phrase, vous aurez quelques secondes pour deviner la forme infinitive du verbe utilisé dans la phrase.

a) Nous finissons nos dessins.
We are finishing our drawings.

_____.

b) Ils créent des concepts artistiques.
They create art concepts.

_____.

c) Je choisis mes amis.
I choose my friends.

_____.

d) Vous saisissez le sens général.
You (pl.) grasp the general meaning.

_____.

e) La banque transfère des fonds aux investisseurs.
The bank transfers funds to investors.

_____.

IMPERFECT
L'IMPARFAIT

You already know when to use the imperfect. It is a tense used to tell or narrate past events. So let us see how it is built. You are in luck with the imperfect tense: *all verbs have the same endings in the imperfect tense of the indicative mode, whether they belong to the first, second, or third group! And there are no exceptions!*

Rather than just showing you the endings on their own, we show you the endings in context with examples. The endings are highlighted.

Imperfect endings for verbs of the first group:

The highlighted endings are the same for every verb of the first group. There is no exception.

SAUTER	TO JUMP
je saut**ais**	I was jumping
tu saut**ais**	you were jumping
il/elle/on saut**ait**	he/she/it was jumping
nous saut**ions**	we were jumping
vous saut**iez**	you (plural) were jumping
ils/elles saut**aient**	they were jumping

Imperfect endings for verbs of the second group:

ROUGIR	TO BLUSH
je rougiss**ais**	I was blushing
tu rougiss**ais**	you were blushing
il/elle/on rougiss**ait**	he/she/it was blushing
nous rougiss**ions**	we were blushing
vous rougiss**iez**	you were blushing
ils/elles rougiss**aient**	they were blushing

Third group:

ALLER	TO GO
j'all**ais**	I was going
tu all**ais**	you were going
il/elle/on all**ait**	he/she/it was going
nous all**ions**	we were going
vous all**iez**	you were going
ils/elles all**aient**	they were going

 **EXERCISES**
EXERCICES

2) Write the verbs in the imperfect tense of the indicative mode.
Mettez les verbes à l'imparfait de l'indicatif.

Quand j'_____(être / to be) petit, je _____(manger / to eat)

des céréales au petit déjeuner et je _____(regarder / to watch)

les dessins animés avant d'aller à l'école. Ensuite, j'_____(aller / to go) à

l'école primaire et je _____(jouer / to play) avec mes amis.

Translation:

When I was a child, I had cereal for breakfast, and I watched cartoons before going to school.
Then I went to primary school and played with my friends.

PERFECT
LE PASSÉ COMPOSE

You are very familiar with this tense by now. Let us revise with an exercise.

EXERCISES
EXERCICES

3) Underline the verbs conjugated in the perfect tense.
Soulignez les verbes conjugués au passé composé.

> J'ai sorti les poubelles. Ensuite, je suis allé marcher dans le parc. Puis finalement, j'ai décidé
>
> de faire un peu de sport donc je suis allé au stade où j'ai couru pendant presque une heure.

Translation:

I took out the trash. Then, I went and had a walk in the park. Then, in the end, I decided to exercise a little, so I went to the stadium where I ran for almost an hour.

SIMPLE PAST
LE PASSÉ SIMPLE

You will not start using this tense unless you start writing French content in the high register. You do not need to know those endings at an upper beginner to lower intermediate level. Being able to recognize the endings is always a good thing but make sure you master the more simple tenses we have covered in this book:

a) the present tense of the indicative mode,

b) the simple future tense,

c) the perfect tense, the near future with **aller + infinitive verb** (**Je vais bientôt partir**. */ I will leave soon.*),

d) and finally, the near past with **venir de + infinitive verb** (**Je viens de nettoyer l'appartement**. */ I just cleaned the flat.*).

The simple past of verbs that belong to the first group is built as such: **root + the endings**. Here is an example with the verb **accepter** *(to accept)*:

ACCEPTER	TO ACCEPT
Radical : **accept**	Root: **accept**
j'accept**ai**	I accepted
tu accept**as**	you accepted
il/elle/on accept**a**	he/she/it accepted
nous accept**âmes**	we accepted
vous accept**âtes**	you accepted
ils/elles accept**èrent**	they accepted

Do not forget the ^ on the a for the first- and second-person plurals.

The simple past of verbs that belong to the second group is built as such: **root + the endings**. Here is an example with the verb **nourrir** *(to feed)*:

NOURRIR	TO FEED
Radical: **nourr**	Root: **nourr**
je nourr**is**	I fed
tu nourr**is**	you fed
il/elle/on nourr**it**	he/she/it fed
nous nourr**îmes**	we fed
vous nourr**îtes**	you fed
ils/elles nourr**irent**	they fed

For verbs belonging to the third group, there are three kinds of endings only:

a) is, -is, -it , -îmes, -îtes, -irent

For example:

FAIRE	TO MAKE / TO DO
je f**is**	I made
tu f**is**	you made
il/elle/on f**it**	he/she/it made
nous f**îmes**	we made
vous f**îtes**	you made
ils/elles f**irent**	they made

b) us, -us, -ut, -ûmes, -ûtes, -urent.

For example:

DEVOIR	MUST / TO HAVE TO
je d**us**	I had to
tu d**us**	you had to
il/elle/on d**ut**	he/she/it had to
nous d**ûmes**	we had to
vous d**ûtes**	you had to
ils/elles d**urent**	they had to

c) ins, -ins,-int, -înmes, -întes, -inrent.

For example:

DEVENIR	TO BECOME
je dev**ins**	I became
tu dev**ins**	you became
il/elle/on dev**int**	he/she/it became
nous dev**înmes**	we became
vous dev**întes**	you became
ils/elles dev**inrent**	they became

EXERCISES
EXERCICES

4) Fill the gaps with the appropriated verbs.

Remplissez les trous avec les verbes conjugués au passé simple.

Quand Marie-Louise _____ chez les Bourbon, elle _____

un bouquet de fleurs devant la statue de leur ancêtre. La famille la _____.

Ensuite, ils se _____ à table.

SIMPLE FUTURE
LE FUTURE SIMPLE

You are already very familiar with the simple future. You should know it really well by now. Besides, it is also one of the easiest tenses. Indeed, all verbs' endings are the same whether they belong to the first, second, or third group. As a reminder, the simple future is built as such: **radical + endings**. Since you have seen a myriad of examples with first and second group verbs in this book, let us see the endings for a verb belonging to the third group:

VOIR	TO SEE
Radical : **verr**	Root: **verr**
je verr**ai**	I will see
tu verr**as**	you will see
il/elle/on verr**a**	he/she/it will see
nous verr**ons**	we will see
vous verr**ez**	you will see
ils/elles verr**ont**	they will see

EXERCISES
EXERCICES

5) Write the verbs in the simple future.

Mettez les verbes au futur simple.

a) J' (aller): _____.

b) Tu (manger): _____.

c) On (crier): _____.

d) Nous (voir): _____.

e) Vous (conjuguer): _____.

f) Elles (partir): _____.

g) Michel (dormir): _____.

h) Luc et Paul (venir): _____.

PLUPERFECT
LE PLUS-QUE-PARFAIT

As you already know, the pluperfect is used to describe something connected to something that happened in the past. An example in English would be: I went to bed because I had finished the laundry.

In this example, *I had finished the laundry* is something that happened before I went to bed, so we use the pluperfect in French to describe such events.

Building the pluperfect should be easy for you by now. It is a compound tense, so it is built as such: **auxiliary in the imperfect tense + past participle**.

The only complexity is to remember to make the past participle agree with the person in gender and number if the auxiliary used is the verb **être** (*to be*). This simply means you have to remember to add an **e** for the **feminine** and an **s** for the **plural** to the past participle of the verb.

Example with the auxiliary <u>avoir</u>:

MANGER	TO EAT
j'avais mang**é**	I had eaten
tu **avais** mang**é**	you had eaten
il/elle/on **avait** mang**é**	he/she/it had eaten
nous **avions** mang**é**	we had eaten
vous **aviez** mang**é**	you had eaten
ils/elles **avaient** mang**é**	they had eaten

Example with the auxiliary <u>être</u>:

PARTIR	TO LEAVE
j'**étai**s part**i**	I had left
tu **étais** part**i**	you had left
il/on **était** part**i**	he/it had left
nous **étions** part**is**	we had left
vous **étiez** part**is**	you had left
ils **étaient** part**is**	they (masc.) had left

Note that we removed **elle** and **elles** from the table as the past participle agrees with the persons in gender and number. You can notice the **s** at the end of the past participle of the first-, second- and third-person plurals.

Example with the auxiliary __être__ and feminine person:

PARTIR	TO LEAVE
j'**étais** part**ie**	I had left
tu **étais** part**ie**	you had left
elle/on **était** part**ie**	she/it had left
nous **étions** part**ies**	we had left
vous **étiez** part**ies**	you had left
elles **étaient** part**ies**	they had left

Here, you can see the **e** at the past participles and that **il** and **ils** are missing in the third person singulars and plurals. This means that **je**, **tu**, **elle**, **nous**, **vous,** and **elles** are all feminine.

EXERCISES
EXERCICES

6) You will hear a text in French. You will have to underline only the verbs conjugated in the pluperfect tense. There are other verbs conjugated in other tenses in the text.

Vous allez entendre un texte en français. Vous devrez souligner seulement les verbes conjugués au plus-que-parfait. Il y a d'autres verbes conjugués à d'autres temps dans le texte.

Note: *the translation is provided in the Answer Key. You should understand almost everything without a translation, though.*

Ma chère amie,

Quand nous nous sommes vues la dernière fois en vacances, j'étais très triste de devoir partir après une semaine merveilleuse. J'avais espéré pouvoir rester une semaine de plus mais mon patron ne m'a pas autorisée. En tout cas, ce n'est pas grave. Nous nous reverrons bientôt.

Tu te souviens quand nous avions marché le long de la rivière ? Nous avions ensuite fait une pause pour dessiner les beaux papillons que nous voyions sur le chemin. Ensuite, nos amis néerlandais nous avaient cuisiné du poisson à la sauce hollandaise.

J'ai très hâte de te revoir. J'espère que la prochaine fois, nous aurons l'occasion de présenter nos enfants les uns aux autres. Je pense qu'ils s'entendront bien. En plus, tes enfants parlent anglais et mes enfants parlent français. Ce sera une super opportunité pour eux de pratiquer leurs langues vivantes étrangères. Mon fils le plus âgé avait été aux États-Unis quand il était au lycée. Il avait adoré.

Gros bisous et à bientôt,

Danielle

PAST ANTERIOR
LE PASSÉ ANTÉRIEUR

This tense is complex and out of scope for this book. We will still show you the endings and how to build it for science, but you will not have exercises on it. You do not need to learn how to build it, but knowing it exists is important at this stage.

When you know how to conjugate verbs in the simple past tense, building the past anterior tense is really easy because it is also a compound test. The past anterior tense is built as such: auxiliary in the **simple past tense + past participle**. Since it is built with an auxiliary verb, the past participle, as with the pluperfect, must agree in number and gender with the person.

RIRE	TO LAUGH
j'**eu** ri	I had laughed
tu **eus** ri	you had laughed
il/elle/on **eut** ri	he/she/it had laughed
nous **eûmes** ri	we had laughed
vous **eûtes** ri	you had laughed
ils/elles **eurent** ri	they had laughed

NOTE
The simple past and de facto the past anterior are tenses usually learned by students when they reach a B2 (upper intermediate) level.

FUTURE ANTERIOR
LE FUTURE ANTÉRIEUR

The future anterior is also a tense studied by learners when they reach a B2 (upper intermediate) level. Therefore, you do not need to learn it. In previous sections, you have seen why it exists and when it is used, which is enough. You do not need to know how to build it. It is also a compound tense, so building it is not that difficult, though. This section remains purely informational at this stage in your learning journey. The future anterior is built as such: auxiliary verb in the simple future tense + past participle. As usual, the past participle must agree with the person in gender and number if the auxiliary verb is **être**.

For example:

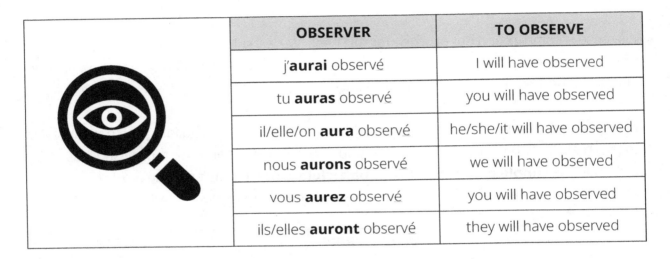

OBSERVER	TO OBSERVE
j'**aurai** observé	I will have observed
tu **auras** observé	you will have observed
il/elle/on **aura** observé	he/she/it will have observed
nous **aurons** observé	we will have observed
vous **aurez** observé	you will have observed
ils/elles **auront** observé	they will have observed

SUBJUNCTIVE
LE SUBJONCTIF

PRESENT
LE PRÉSENT

In this section about the subjunctive mode, the **only** tense you need to master is the present tense. For this reason, the exercise at the end of the section on the tenses of the subjunctive mode will only cover the present tense. You **need to know it well.** You already know when to use it.

As a reminder, when you see **que** followed by a verb, the verb is usually conjugated in the present tense of the subjunctive.

You need to know **one major exception** by heart: after **après que**, the verb that follows is always *conjugated in the present tense of the indicative mode*. Many native speakers of French make this mistake, so it can be confusing at times. However, this is unacceptable, and the indicative should always follow **après que**.

For example:

a) **Correct:** Aprés que je **vais** à l'école, j'achète un sandwich.
   After I go to school, I buy a sandwich.

b) **Very wrong**: Aprés que je **sois** allé à l'école, j'ai acheté un sandwich.
   After I went to school, I bought a sandwich.

The present tense of the subjunctive mode of verbs that belong to the first group is built as such: **root of the indicative + the following endings: e, es, e, ions, iez, ent**. For example:

DONNER	TO GIVE
Radical : **donn**	Root: **donn**
que je donn**e**	that I give
que tu donn**es**	that you give
qu'il/elle/on donn**e**	that he/she/it gives
que nous donn**ions**	that we give
que vous donn**iez**	that you give
qu'ils/elles donn**ent**	that they give

The **same endings** can be applied to verbs of the **second group**, except that instead of just using the root of the infinitive, the extended, **root of the infinitive + iss**, is used. For example:

FINIR	TO FINISH
Radical + iss: **finiss**	Root + iss: **finiss**
que je fin**isse**	that I finish
que tu fin**isses**	that you finish
qu'il/elle/on fin**isse**	that he/she/it finishes
que nous fin**issions**	that we finish
que vous fin**issiez**	that you finish
qu'ils/elles fin**issent**	that they finish

For verbs belonging to the third group, there are three cases, whether:

a) the verb has only **one root** in the present tense of the indicative: the only root is then used to build the present tense of the subjunctive.

b) the verb has **two roots** in the present tense of the indicative: then the present tense of the subjunctive is then built using the *root of the first-person plural of the present tense of the indicative mode.*

c) the verb ends with **oir** or **oire**: then the present tense of the subjunctive is built using *both roots following the rules of the present tense of the indicative.*

The **good news,** though, is that the *endings remain the same for verbs of all categories,* which means they work for irregular verbs too!

Example of a verb with one root in the present tense of the indicative:

COUVRIR	TO COVER
Radical: **couvr**	Root: **couvr**
que je couvr**e**	that I cover
que tu couvr**es**	that you cover
qu'il/elle/on couvr**e**	that he/she/it covers
que nous couvr**ions**	that we cover
que vous couvr**iez**	that you cover
qu'ils/elles couvr**ent**	that they cover

Example of a verb with two roots in the present tense of the indicative:

DORMIR	TO SLEEP
Radical: **dorm** (because nous dormons)	Root: **dorm** (because nous dormons)
que je dorm**e**	that I sleep
que tu dorm**es**	that you sleep
qu'il/elle/on dorm**e**	that he/she/it sleeps
que nous dorm**ions**	that we sleep
que vous dorm**iez**	that you sleep
qu'ils/elles dorm**ent**	that they sleep

Example with a verb that ends with oir or oire:

CROIRE	TO BELIEVE
Radical: **croi** or **croy**	Root: **croi** or **croy**
que je cr**oie**	that I believe
que tu cr**oies**	that you believe
qu'il/elle/on cr**oit**	that he/she/it believes
que nous cr**oyions**	that we believe
que vous cr**oyiez**	that you believe
qu'ils/elles cr**oient**	that they believe

PAST, IMPERFECT, AND PLUPERFECT OF THE SUBJUNCTIVE MODE
LE PASSÉ, L'IMPARFAIT ET LE PLUS-QUE-PARFAIT DU MODE SUBJUNCTIF

These three tenses are barely used whatsoever in the French language. You do not need to learn them. You will only rarely encounter them. We will not go further and explain how to build those tenses. In your learning journey, you may never hear about them again until you reach a C1-C2 (advanced / near native) level, and even then, it might only be the subject of a small section. Most native speakers of French learn how to build those tenses in school but never use them again after. Knowing they exist is one of the only requirements, including in schools of the French-speaking world.

EXERCISES
EXERCICES

1) Write the verbs in the present tense of the subjunctif mood.

Mettez les verbes au présent du subjonctif.

Il faudra que / qu' :

a) tu _____ (avoir) tes affaires.
   You will need to have your things.

b) il _____ (être) prudent.
   He will have to be careful.

c) vous _____ (pouvoir) arriver en avance.
   You (pl.) will have to arrive early.

d) nous _____ (manger) plus tôt demain.
   We will have to eat earlier tomorrow.

e) vous _____ (regarder) le documentaire avant de commencer le cours.
   You (pl.) will have to watch the documentary before starting with the course.

f) ils _____ (faire) attention à ne pas tomber pendant la séance d'escalade.
   They will have to be careful not to fall during the climbing session.

g) nous _____ (repartir) avant la tombée de la nuit.
   We will have to go back before nightfall.

h) il leur _____ (dire) exactement ce qu'il attend d'eux.
   He will have to explain clearly what he expects from them.

i) tu me _____ (raconter) cette fameuse histoire.
You will have to tell me that story.

j) tu lui _____ (offrir) un cadeau pour la Saint-Valentin.
You will have to offer him/her a present for Valentine's Day.

k) l'on _____ (se réunir) pour le Nouvel An chinois.
We will have to gather together for the Chinese New Year.

CONDITIONAL

LE CONDITIONNEL

There are **two tenses** in the conditional mode: **present** and **past**. Usually, the present tense of the conditional mode is taught to students who already have a B1 (intermediate) level in French. The past tense of the conditional is usually taught to students who have a B2 level already. If you properly know and understand the concepts we told you were important, you should have reached a B1 level by now. Therefore, we will show you the endings of the present tense of the conditional mode and one example for reference.

The present tense of the conditional mode is built using the root of the verb conjugated in the simple future + the endings of the imperfect. For example:

ESSAYER	TO TRY
Root of the simple future: **essayer**	Root of the simple future: **essayer**
j'essayer**ais**	I would try
tu essayer**ais**	you would try
il/elle/on essayer**ait**	he/she/it would try
nous essayer**ions**	we would try
vous essayer**iez**	you would try
ils/elles essayer**aient**	they would try

IMPERATIVE
L'IMPÉRATIF

Welcome to the last section of this book. The present tense of the imperative mode is a must know for a beginner in French. It is usually taught to learners who have never learned any French before, A1 (beginner, first time learning French). Building it is very easy, though. You already know when to use it, to express orders, pieces of advice, etc. It can be used only with the **second-person singular** and the **first- and second-person plurals**. It is built by *removing the subject, taking the root of the present tense of the indicative*, and *adding the following endings*: -**e or -s, -ons, -ez.**

The present tense of the imperative mode of the verbs **avoir**, **être**, **savoir**, and **vouloir** is built using the root of the subjunctive rather than the indicative. *The endings remain the same.*

Now, in the endings, you saw **e** or **s,** why is that? For the *second person singular* **tu**, verbs that belong to the first group end in **e** while all others end in **s** except **avoir,** which ends in **e** in the second person singular. In the first example, the subjects are between parentheses so that you know which subject the conjugated forms belong to, but they disappear when writing or speaking in the imperative. We do not include the subjects anymore after the first example. You will understand better with examples.

The verb <u>avoir</u> (*to have*):

Avoir	To have
Root of the subjunctive: **ai** or **ay**	Root of the subjunctive: **ai** or **ay**
(tu) ai**e** !	have!
(nous) ay**ons** !	let us have!
(vous) ay**ez** !	have (pl.)!
Example sentence: **Aie du courage** ! / *Have some guts!*	

The verb <u>être</u> (*to be*):

ÊTRE	TO BE
Root of the subjunctive: **soi** or **soy**	Root of the subjunctive: soi or soy
soi**s** !	be!
soy**ons** !	let us be!
soy**ez** !	be (pl.)!
Example sentence: **Sois poli(e)** ! / *Be polite!*	

Example of a verb of the first group:

FERMER	TO CLOSE
Root: **ferm**	Root: **ferm**
ferm**e** !	close!
ferm**ons** !	let us close!
ferm**ez** !	close (pl.)!
Example sentence: **Fermons la porte** ! / *Let us close the door!*	

Example of verb of the second group:

FINIR	TO FINISH
Root: **finis**	Root: **finis**
fini**s** !	finish!
finis**sons** !	let us finish!
finis**sez** !	finish (pl.)!
Example: **Finissez vos devoirs** ! / *Finish (pl.) your homework!*	

Example with a verb of the third group:

FAIRE	TO DO (OR TO MAKE)
Root: **fai**	Root: **fai**
fai**s** !	do!
fai**sons** !	let us do!
fai**tes** !	do (pl.)
Example sentence: **Faisons la vaisselle** ! / *Let us wash the dishes!*	

EXERCISES
EXERCICES

1) Listen and put the verbs in the present tense of the imperative.
Écoutez et mettez les verbes au présent de l'impératif.

a) _____ (mettre) nos manteaux !
   Let us put our coats on.

b) _____ (laisser) les clefs sur la porte.
   Leave (sing.) the keys on the door.

c) _____ (sortir) les poubelles demain matin.
   Take (sing.) the trash out tomorrow morning!

d) _____ (venir) me voir dans mon bureau à 15h.
   Come (pl.) to my office at 3 PM.

CONCLUSION

CONCLUSION

Congratulations, you have made it to the end of this book. You can be proud of yourself. This book is probably amongst the most complex books you used in your learning journey, since grammar is often perceived as complex by foreign languages learners.

By now, you should have an A2+ - B1 level (upper beginner – lower intermediate) level. You understand all basic concepts such as the verbs **être** and **avoir**. In addition, you now know what the infinitive, regular, and irregular verbs are.

You know all the categories a verb can belong to, transitive, intransitive, pronominal, auxiliary, etc. You also know about the modes and the values of their respective tenses.

Finally, you know how to conjugate verbs in the most common tenses: the present, the imperfect, the perfect, the simple future, and the pluperfect of the indicative mode. You also know how to conjugate verbs in the present tense of the subjunctive and imperative modes.

If you understand all the categories, the modes and their values, the imperfect, and the pluperfect well, you probably have a B1 (lower intermediate) level by now. If you still struggle with the concepts we just mentioned, you probably have at least an A2+ (upper beginner) level by now. Even if you do not understand all those concepts well yet, do not worry; go back to the concepts that are still unclear and review challenging content. There is only one small step between A2+ (upper beginner) and B1 (lower intermediate). You can do it!

We hope that you had fun learning about French verbs with Lingo Mastery. We have tried to make it as fun yet enriching as possible by avoiding endless conjugation tables, providing you with some useful and funny examples, and by explaining complex concepts using simple terms. Grammar, including conjugation, does not have to be tedious and difficult! We wish you good luck and enjoyment in the rest of your learning journey. Au revoir!

Au revoir!

ANSWER KEY
RÉPONSES AUX EXERCICES

THE BASICS
LES BASES

To be / to have – *être / avoir*

1) a) suis
  b) es
  c) est
  d) sommes
  e) êtes
  f) sont

2) a) ai
  b) as
  c) a
  d) avons
  e) avez
  f) ont

3) a) suis   **o)** sont
  b) avons   **p)** a
  c) n'ont   **q)** Être / être
  d) avez   **r)** est
  e) a   **s)** est
  f) es   **t)** ont
  g) ont
  h) suis
  i) est
  j) a
  k) est
  l) est
  m) ont
  n) a

Infinitive / *Infinitif*

1) a) manger
   b) courir
   c) avoir
   d) faire
   e) compter
   f) écouter

2) a) m'aider
   b) marcher
   c) dormir
   d) voir
   e) découvrir
   f) être
   g) coudre
   h) faire
   i) nager
   j) monter

Regular / Irregular – *Régulier / Irrégulier*

1) First part of the exercise:
   a) nager
   b) danser
   c) effacer
   d) percer
   e) voyager
   f) payer

Second part:
   a) nagez
   b) paie
   c) effacent
   d) voyageons
   e) danses
   f) perçons

Active and passive voices / *Voix passives et actives*

1) a) Les comédiens de la troupe de théâtre ont été applaudis par le public.
   The comedians of the drama company are applauded by the public.

   b) Une fête de fin d'année sera organisée par l'école primaire.
   An end of the year party will be organized by the primary school.

   c) Ce système informatique sera utilisé pendant plusieurs années à l'université.
   This IT system will be used for several years at the university.

   d) Des immeubles seront construits au bord de la mer par l'entreprise.
   Buildings will be built by the company by the seaside.

   e) L'élève a été accusé alors qu'il n'avait rien fait.
   The pupil was accused even though he had not done anything.

   f) Toutes les tomates de mon jardin ont été mangées par les insectes et les oiseaux.
   All the tomatoes of my garden were eaten by insects and birds.

   g) Il sera sûrement nommé premier ministre par le nouveau président.
   He will probably be appointed as the prime minister by the new president.

   h) Une nouvelle zone industrielle a été aménagée par le maire pour promouvoir l'emploi.
   A new industrial zone will be developed by the mayor to promote employment.

   i) Un médicament contre une maladie infectieuse a été découvert par le scientifique.
   A treatment against an infectious disease was discovered by the scientist.

   j) Des randonneurs suisses et belges ont été surpris par une tempête explosive.
   Some Swiss and Belgian hikers were surprised by an explosive storm.

Most used tenses / *Les temps les plus usités*

1) a) Les feuilles des arbres **jaunissent** rapidement en automne.
   b) Les jus de fruits **vieillissent** mal au frigo.
   c) Les juristes **punissent** les criminels.
   d) Le public **applaudit** les soignants.
   e) Nous **agissons** toujours trop lentement.
   f) Je **hais** la méchanceté.
   g) Les voitures **ralentissent** au feu orange.

CLASSIFICATION OF VERBS
LA CLASSIFICATION DES VERBES

Transitive and intransitive verbs / Les verbes transitifs et intransitifs

1) **a)** transitif-direct
   b) transitif-indirect
   c) transitive-indirect
   d) transitive-direct
   e) transitive-indirect
   f) transitive-indirect
   g) intransitive
   h) transitive-indirect
   i) transitive-indirect
   j) transitive-indirect
   k) transitive-direct
   l) transitive-direct
   m) transitive-direct
   n) transitive-direct
   o) intransitive

p) transitive-direct
q) intransitive
r) transitive-indirect
s) transitive-direct
t) transitive-direct

Impersonal verbs / Les verbes impersonnels

1) **a)** il pleut, il faut
   b) Il suffit de
   c) Il reste

d) Il paraît
e) il vaut mieux
f) il fait, il y a

Reflexive verbs / Les verbes réfléchis

1) **a)** se réveille
   b) se lève
   c) se dépêcher

d) se promener
e) s'inquiète

Copular verbs / Les verbes copules

1) **a)** Action verb.
   b) Attributive verb.

c) Attributive verb.
d) Attributive verb.

e) Action verb.

Auxiliary verbs / *Les verbes auxiliaires*

1) a) sont
  b) sommes
  c) a
  d) a
  e) est

Semi-auxiliary verbs / *Les verbes semi-auxiliaires*

1) a) viens
  b) faut
  c) viennent
  d) faut
  e) fais
  f) allons

Phrasal verbs / *Les locutions verbales*

1) a) This coat fits you like a glove!
  b) The businessman is chasing after money.
  c) We are extending a helping hand to all our colleagues in these difficult times.
  d) He is in a hurry.
  e) My friends don't mince their words.

MOODS
LES MODES

Personal moods / *Les modes personnels*

1) a) Mode: Conditional; Tense: Present

   b) Mode: Present Participle; Tense: Present

   c) Mode: Conditional; Tense: Compound Past

   d) Mode: Subjunctive; Tense: Present

   e) Mode: Imperative; Tense: Present

   f) Mode: Imperfect; Tense: Compound Past

   g) Mode: Conditional; Tense: Imperfect Subjunctive

   h) Mode: Gerund; Tense: Present

   i) Mode: Indicative; Tense: Past Simple

   j) Mode: Conditional; Tense: Compound Past

   k) Mode: Present Participle; Tense: Compound Past

   l) Mode: Future Simple; Tense: Future

   m) Mode: Conditional; Tense: Imperfect

   n) Mode: Imperative; Tense: Present

   o) Mode: Imperative; Tense: Present

   Mode: Indicative; Tense: Future

REGULAR AND IRREGULAR VERBS
LES VERBES RÉGULIERS ET IRRÉGULIERS

1) Ce matin, mes enfants, Dominique et Henri, **sont allés** à l'école à bicyclette. À l'école, ils **font** souvent des activités ludiques comme de la peinture, du sport, de la sculpture, et même des gâteaux en cours de cuisine. Ce que Dominique **préfère**, c'est **jouer** au badminton en cours de sport. Henri, lui, **préfère** les cours d'arts plastiques. Il **peint** déjà énormément en temps normal à la maison.

La semaine prochaine, tous les élèves de leur classe **vont partir** en Angleterre en voyage de classe. La maîtresse d'école **a demandé** à deux parents d'élèves de **venir** avec eux. J'ai proposé de **venir** et cela **a été accepté**, donc c'est sûr, j'y **vais** !

Apparemment, il **pleut** souvent en Angleterre, on **verra** bien le temps une fois sur place. Puis, nous **allons voyager** à travers tout le pays donc le temps ne sera sûrement pas le même partout.

Quand les élèves **reviendront** en cours, ils **seront** sûrement tristes d'avoir quitté l'Angleterre. Ils **ont** tous hâte d'y **aller**.

Le seul problème **est** que les enfants **dorment** dans des familles chez leurs correspondants. Pour nous, les deux parents d'élèves accompagnateurs, rien **n'a** encore **été** prévu. Cependant, je **suis** sûre que ce problème **sera résolu** rapidement.

Translation

This morning, my children, Dominique, and Henri, **went** to school by bike. At school, they often **do** fun activities such as painting, sports, sculpture, and even cakes during cooking classes. What Dominique **prefers** is **playing** badminton in sports class. Henri, on the other hand, **prefers** art classes. He already usually **paints** a lot at home.

Next week, all the students in their class **will go** to England on a class trip. The schoolteacher **asked** two parents **to come** with them. I offered to **come,** and it **was accepted**, so **I'm** definitely **going**!

Apparently, it often **rains** in England, we **will see** how the weather is once we are there we **will travel** across the country so the weather **will** certainly not **be** the same everywhere.

When the students **return** to school, they **will** surely **be** sad to have left England. They **are** all **looking** forward to it.

The only problem **is** that children **sleep** at their correspondents' families. For us, the two accompanying parents, nothing **has been** planned yet. However, I **am** sure that this problem **will be resolved** quickly.

TENSES
LES TEMPS

1) a) Finir   **d)** Saisir

    b) Créer   **e)** Transférer

    c) Choisir

2) Quand **j'étais** petit, je **mangeais** des céréales au petit déjeuner et je **regardais** les dessins animés avant d'aller à l'école. Ensuite, **j'allais** à l'école primaire et je **jouais** avec mes amis.

3) J'**ai sorti** les poubelles. Ensuite, je **suis allé** marcher dans le parc. Puis finalement, j'**ai décidé** de faire un peu de sport donc je **suis allé** au stade où j'**ai couru** pendant presque une heure.

4) Quand Marie-Louise **arriva** chez les Bourbon, elle **déposa** un bouquet de fleurs devant la statue de leur ancêtre. La famille la **remercia**. Ensuite, ils se **mirent** à table.

5) a) irai   **e)** conjuguerez

    b) mangeras   **f)** partiront

    c) criera   **g)** dormira

    d) verrons   **h)** viendront

6) Ma chère amie,

Quand nous nous sommes vues la dernière fois en vacances, j'étais très triste de devoir partir après une semaine merveilleuse. **J'avais espéré pouvoir rester** une semaine de plus mais mon patron ne m'a pas autorisée. En tout cas, ce n'est pas grave. Nous nous reverrons bientôt.

Tu te souviens quand **nous avions marché** le long de la rivière ? **Nous avions ensuite fait** une pause pour dessiner les beaux papillons que nous voyions sur le chemin. Ensuite, nos amis néerlandais nous **avaient cuisiné** du poisson à la sauce hollandaise.

J'ai très hâte de te revoir. J'espère que la prochaine fois, nous aurons l'occasion de présenter nos enfants les uns aux autres. Je pense qu'ils s'entendront bien. En plus, tes enfants parlent anglais et mes enfants parlent français. Ce sera une super opportunité pour eux de pratiquer leurs langues vivantes étrangères. Mon fils le plus âgé **avait été** aux États-Unis quand il était au lycée. Il avait adoré.

Gros bisous et à bientôt, Danielle

My dear friend (fem.),

When we saw each other the last time while on holidays, I was so sad I had to leave after a wonderful week. I had hoped to be able to stay another week, but my boss did not allow me to. It is not a big deal though. We will see each other again soon.

Do you remember when we walked along the river? We then took a break to draw the beautiful butterflies we saw on the way. Then, our Dutch friends cooked some fish with Hollandaise.

I cannot wait to see you again. I hope that next time, we can introduce our children to each other. Besides, your children speak English and my children Speak French. It will be an opportunity for them to practice the languages they learn at school. My oldest son went to the United States when he was in high school. He loved it there.

Kisses and see you soon, Danielle

Subjunctive / *Le subjonctif*

1) a) aies
   b) soit
   c) puissiez
   d) mangions
   e) regardiez
   f) fassent
   g) repartions
   h) dise
   i) racontes
   j) offres
   k) réunisse

Imperative / *L'impératif*

1) a) Mettons
   b) Laisse
   c) Sors
   d) Venez

LIST OF IRREGULAR VERBS

VERBS / VERBES	ENGLISH / ANGLAIS
Abattre	*to knock down*
Absoudre	*to absolve*
Abstenir (s')	*abstain (to)*
Acheter	*to buy*
Accroître	*to grow*
Accueillir	*to welcome*
Acquérir	*to acquire*
Aller	*to go*
Apercevoir	*to notice*
Apparaître	*to appear*
Appartenir	*to belong to*
Appeler	*to call*
Apprécier	*to appreciate*
Apprendre	*to learn*
Assaillir	*to mob*
Asseoir (s') on utilise surtout la forme pronominale de sens réfléchi s'asseoir	*to sit, mainly used with "s'" as the pronominal form of reflexive meaning*
Assiéger	*to besiege*
Atteindre	*to reach*
Avoir	*to have*
Battre	*to beat*
Boire	*to drink*
Bouillir	*to boil*
Broyer	*to crush*
Céder	*to surrender*
Clore	*to close*
Combattre	*to fight*
Commencer	*to begin*
Comparaître	*to appear before (a judge)*

Comprendre	*to understand*
Compromettre	*to jeopardize*
Concevoir	*to design*
Conclure	*to conclude*
Concourir	*to compete*
Conduire	*to drive*
Confire	*to preserve / comfit*
Connaître	*to know*
Conquérir	*to conquer*
Construire	*to build*
Contenir	*to contain*
Contredire	*to contradict*
Convaincre	*to convince*
Convenir	*to agree*
Coudre	*to sew*
Courir	*to run*
Couvrir	*to cover*
Craindre	*to fear*
Croire	*to believe*
Croître	*to grow*
Cueillir	*to pluck*
Cuire	*to cook*
Déceler	*to identify*
Décevoir	*to deceive*
Découvrir	*to discover*
Décrire	*to describe*
Déduire	*to deduct*
Défaire	*to undo*
Déplaire	*to displease*
Détruire	*to destroy*
Devenir	*to become*
Devoir	*must*

Dire	*to say*
Disparaître	*to disappear*
Dissoudre	*to dissolve*
Distraire	*to distract*
Dormir	*to sleep*
Eclore	*to hatch out*
Écrire	*to write*
Élire	*to elect*
Émettre	*to emit*
Employer	*to employ*
Enclore	*to enclose in*
Enfuir (s')	*to run away*
Entreprendre	*to undertake*
Entretenir	*to maintain*
Envoyer	*to send*
Equivaloir	*to amount to*
Éteindre	*to turn off*
Être	*to be*
Exclure	*to exclude*
Extraire	*to extract*
Faillir	*to fail in something*
Faire	*to do / to make*
Falloir	*must*
Feindre	*to sham*
Fuir	*to escape*
Geler	*to freeze*
Haïr	*to hate*
Haleter	*to pant*
Harceler	*to harass*
Inclure	*to include*
Inscrire	*to enroll / register*
Instruire	*to instruct / train*

Interdire	*to forbid*
Intervenir	*to intervene*
Introduire	*to introduce*
Jeter	*to throw away*
Joindre	*to join*
Lancer	*to launch*
Lever	*to raise*
Lire	*to read*
Luire	*to shine*
Maintenir	*to maintain*
Manger	*to eat*
Méconnaître	*to misjudge*
Médire	*to badmouth*
Méprendre (se)	*to misunderstand / to be mistaken*
Mettre	*to put*
Modeler	*to form*
Moudre	*to grind*
Mourir	*to die*
Mouvoir	*to move*
Naître	*to be born*
Nuire	*to harm*
Obtenir	*to obtain*
Offrir	*to offer*
Omettre	*to omit*
Ouvrir	*to open*
Paître	*to graze*
Paraître	*to seem*
Parcourir	*to browse, cross*
Parvenir	*to attain*
Payer	*to pay*
Peindre	*to paint*
Peler	*to skin*

Percevoir	*to perceive*
Permettre	*to allow*
Peser	*to weigh*
Placer	*to place*
Plaindre	*to complain*
Plaire	*to please*
Pleuvoir	*to rain*
Poursuivre	*to pursue*
Pourvoir	*to fill / provide for something*
Pouvoir	*to be able to*
Prédire	*to predict*
Prendre	*to take*
Prescrire	*to prescribe*
Prévaloir	*to prevail over*
Prévenir	*to prevent*
Prévoir	*to forecast*
Promettre	*to promise*
Recevoir	*to receive*
Reconnaître	*to acknowledge*
Recueillir	*to gather*
Réduire	*to reduce*
Rejoindre	*to join*
Renaître	*to be reborn*
Renvoyer	*to resend*
Résoudre	*to resolve*
Restreindre	*to restrict*
Revoir	*to review*
Rire	*to laugh*
Rompre	*to break up*
Satisfaire	*to satisfy*
Savoir	*to know*
Séduire	*to seduce*

Sentir	*to smell / feel*
Servir	*to serve*
Souffrir	*to suffer*
Soumettre	*to submit*
Sourire	*to smile*
Souscrire	*to subscribe*
Soutenir	*to support*
Souvenir (se)	*to remember*
Suffire	*to suffice*
Suivre	*to follow*
Surprendre	*to surprise*
Survenir	*to occur*
Survivre	*to survive*
Taire	*to keep quiet*
Taire (se)	*to keep quiet*
Teindre	*to dye*
Tenir	*to hold*
Transcrire	*to transcribe*
Transmettre	*to transmit*
Tressaillir	*to shudder / shake / tremble*
Vaincre	*to defeat*
Valoir	*to be worth*
Venir	*to come*
Vêtir	*to dress*
Vivre	*to live*
Voir	*to see*
Vouloir	*to want*

MORE BOOKS BY LINGO MASTERY

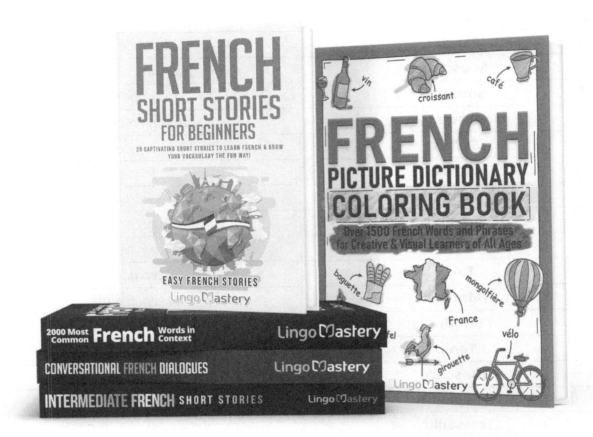

We are not done teaching you French until you're fluent!

Here are some other titles you might find useful in your journey of mastering French:

✓ French Short Stories for Beginners

✓ Intermediate French Short Stories

✓ 2000 Most Common French Words in Context

✓ Conversational French Dialogues

But we got many more!

Check out all of our titles at **www.LingoMastery.com/french**

Made in the USA
Columbia, SC
22 January 2024